迪特·拉姆斯
设计箴言

Less but Better

〔德〕迪特·拉姆斯 著　杨继梅 译

北京科学技术出版社

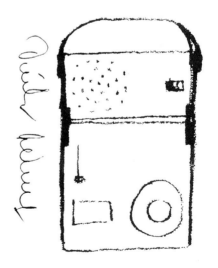

Dieter
Rams

著作权合同登记号　图字: 01-2022-0106

图书在版编目（CIP）数据

迪特·拉姆斯设计箴言 /（德）迪特·拉姆斯著；
杨继梅译. —北京：北京科学技术出版社，2022.6（2024.9 重印）
ISBN 978-7-5714-2138-0

Ⅰ. ①迪… Ⅱ. ①迪… ②杨… Ⅲ. ①工业设计
Ⅳ. ①TB47

中国版本图书馆CIP数据核字（2022）第033788号

策划编辑：李　菲
责任编辑：李　菲
文字编辑：李　琳
责任校对：贾　荣
责任印制：李　茗
图文制作：北京锋尚制版有限公司
出 版 人：曾庆宇
出版发行：北京科学技术出版社
社　　址：北京西直门南大街16号
邮政编码：100035
电　　话：0086-10-66135495（总编室）　0086-10-66113227（发行部）
网　　址：www.bkydw.cn
印　　刷：北京华联印刷有限公司
开　　本：889 mm × 1194 mm　1/16
字　　数：200 千字
印　　张：10.25
版　　次：2022年6月第1版
印　　次：2024年9月第2次印刷
ISBN 978-7-5714-2138-0

定　　价：199.00元

本书献给博朗（Braun）公司的全体员工，他们在我40年的工作生涯中一直积极支持、配合我，协助我保持了博朗设计的最初形式。同时，他们也将继续推动博朗设计未来的发展。

迪特·拉姆斯　1995年

This book is dedicated to all the staff at Braun AG who, during my 40 years of design at the company, have worked enthusiastically with me, supported me and helped me to maintain Braun design in its originally intended form and who will continue to develop it into the future.

Dieter Rams 1995

第5版前言

本书第一次出版时正值我生命中的一个转折点：我因年纪大了而于1997年结束了在博朗公司的工作，同时也停止了在汉堡美术学院（HfBK Hamburg）的教学工作。我更愿意说成"不得不结束"，因为我在20年前根本还没有退休养老的想法，即使到了现在我仍然没有这个想法。

因此，我从未打算将这本书写成对历史的回顾，而是写成出自我创意设计立场的一个"艺术宣言"。这在当时所谓的后现代主义后期并不是特别流行，因为当时人们认为事物代表的意义与语义比它们的使用性或功能更重要。

本书能够出版，乔·克拉特功不可没，是他激励我去出版本书。在他的大力支持下，其出版公司已经出版了4版，3次再版。因此，我要特别感谢这位出版商兼平面设计师，由他主编的德国知名杂志《设计＋设计》（*Design+Design*）对于记载和传播博朗公司的优秀设计历史做出了重大贡献。

本书的第5版由柏林的形式出版社（Die Gestalten Verlag）出版，新版经重新翻译、校对后采用了更先进的印刷技术，但是书中内容保持不变，所有的再版修订工作都是在乔·克拉特的监审下制作完成的。此次再版是为了补充一些真实的原始材料，以便进一步丰富既有的关于设计内容的文字叙述。在我看来，本书是内容全面的专题出版物，推荐将其作为目前市面上由惠子（Keiko Ueki）和克劳斯·克莱姆（Klaus Klemp）编著的《迪特·拉姆斯：少与多》（*Less and More*），以及由索菲·洛弗尔（Sophie Lovell）编著的《迪特·拉姆斯：尽可能少的设计》（*Dieter Rams: as little design as possible*）两本书的资料补充。

设计是一面反映社会文化和状况的镜子，所以它的形式是一直变化的。自后现代主义出现以来，设计语言已经发生了变化。在全球化不断扩张的今天，产品的实用性和耐用性变得更加重要。原因有两方面：一是我们的资源是有限的，二是产品消费过程中的参与者也是不断增加的。对我来说，设计的目的不是为了迎合奢侈的购买动机，而是为了给这样一个复杂难懂又引人入胜的大千世界提供一个方向和行为引导系统。设计的目的在于认真地思考如何让这个世界变得更好，如何为每个人提供更值得去好好生活的明天。

荣誉教授、荣誉博士，迪特·拉姆斯
2013年12月

Preface to the 5th Edition

This book was first published at a time that marked a changing point in my life. One in which, thanks to my age, I ended both my employment at Braun and my teaching post at the HfBK Hamburg in 1997. Although I would prefer to say "had to end", since I was by no means in the mood for retirement almost 20 years ago and am still not today.

Therefore this book was never intended to be a retrospective, rather a "state of the art" of my creative position. It was not a particularly popular undertaking in the latter period of so-called postmodernism, when the meanings of things, their semantics, were taken to be more important than their usability, or function.

It is to Jo Klatt's credit that he motivated me to take on this publication, and it is he who has supported it through four editions with his own publishing company. Therefore I owe a very special thankyou to this publisher and graphic designer who, as editor of the magazine Design+Design, has done so much to establish the merit of the Braun company design history.

This fifth edition, now published by "Die Gestalten Verlag" in Berlin, has been re-translated, re-proof-read and technically optimised for print, but the content remains unchanged and all has been done under the watchful eye of Jo Klatt. The intention is to enrich the current discourse about design with some authentic source material. To my eyes this book serves as a supplement to the comprehensive and commendable monographic publications from Keiko Ueki and Klaus Klemp (Less and More), and from Sophie Lovell (Dieter Rams: as little design as possible).

The design discourse paradigms have changed since postmodernism, as they are always changing, because design is also the materialised mirror of any cultural and social condition. Today, in the time of expanded globalisation, the usefulness and durability of products play a far greater role than before. One the one hand our resources are limited, and on the other, the number of participants in the consumption process is constantly increasing. Design for me is not about pandering to luxury buying incentives, but producing orientation-and behavioural-systems for a complex and complicated, yet simultaneously fascinating, open world. It is about seriously considering how to make this world a place where we can offer a tomorrow worth living for everyone.

Prof. em. Dr. mult h.c. Dieter Rams
December 2013

第1版前言

1994年，我参加了一场迪特·拉姆斯先生的讲座，出席讲座的是他的学生和同事。在这之后不久我就意识到，他在这场讲座中所展示的那些图片、说明文字，以及围绕着"设计的未来"（The Future of Design）主题所阐述的内容不应该被限定在这么小的现场范围内，而是应该被更多对此主题感兴趣的人们知道。

因此，我开始尝试说服迪特·拉姆斯先生发表他的讲座报告。尽管他一开始很不情愿，但他对于发表的兴趣却一直在增长。后来，发表讲座报告的计划逐渐发展为编著一本完整的书，这意味着最初讲座中的那些幻灯片和文稿已经无法满足新的需求了，所有东西都需要被重新编辑和调整。因此，本书的出版日期不得不推迟两次。

尽管本书的编辑过程几经周折，但它并不是对博朗公司历史的全面回顾。正如拉姆斯所说，这只是一份"期中报告"。本书点明了拉姆斯的几个关键设计阶段，同时还对大量相关的设计产品进行了概述，但它并不是也不可能是一本完整的资料汇编。

书中包含很多图片，它们显示了拉姆斯在博朗公司的所有主要产品线的设计发展。他在这一时期所设计的杰出作品直至今日依然堪称经典。拉姆斯所开发的大量极具创新性的产品都集中在音源功放的高保真（hi-fi）设备领域，当时正处于从旧的电子管技术到较新的晶体管技术的过渡期，这让他有机会创造出堪称艺术品的电器产品。其中，特别突出的作品包括袖珍收音机T 3、T 31、T 4和T 41，以及P 1唱片机。如果不是那些完全过时的电子元件泄露了它们的真实年代，这些电器的经典设计即使是在今天也绝对会在市场上占有一席之地。

关于这本书，我最后要说的是，迪特·拉姆斯的设计总是以他所坚信的"好的设计是所有精心设计的细节的总和"而

Introduction to the 1st Edition

In 1994 I attended a slide lecture that Dieter Rams gave to his students and academic colleagues. It didn't take me long to realise that the images he was showing, the explanatory text and of course the main part of his lecture entitled "The Future of Design" should not be restricted to a small group of listeners, but had to be made available to anyone interested in the subject.

I tried to convince Dieter Rams to publish his lecture. He was reluctant at first, but his interest grew. The project began to develop into an entire book, but by then the original slides and text alone did not match the new requirements. Everything was revised and reworked. As a result, the publication date had to be postponed twice.

Despite all the tribulations involved, this book should in no way be considered a comprehensive retrospective of the company history of Braun. It is intended to be, as Dieter Rams himself says, an interim statement. It indicates key design phases and outlines a wealth of products, but doesn't even pretend to be a complete documentation.

The many illustrations show the development of design in all the main product lines at Braun. Exceptional designs developed here are considered design classics today. A large number of the most innovative products that Rams worked on were in the hi-fi appliance area during the transition from old valves to the newer transistor technology. During this period he had the chance to create appliances that are almost objects of art in their own right. Particularly outstanding are the pocket-receivers T 3, T 31, T 4 and the T 41 as well as the P 1 record player. The timeless design of these appliances would definitely stand a chance in today's market, were it not for the totally outdated electronics that give away their true age.

One last remark about this book: Dieter Rams' design is always distinguished by his belief that good design is the sum of all well-designed details. He talks of "thorough

著称。他谈到了"彻底的设计"。通过本书，你会发现迪特·拉姆斯拥有建筑学背景。他认为，建筑不只与外墙立面的设计有关，还应包括整栋建筑的所有其他设计。不仅如此，他还提倡对从建筑配件、固定装置到家具等一系列要素给予同等关注，尤其是家具和日常用品，更应考虑到为用户提供服务。无论是产品设计还是建筑设计，迪特·拉姆斯始终认为它们的设计态度和设计品质的本质是一致的。

乔·克拉特（Jo Klatt）
1995年4月

design". Here you can recognise his architectural background. Architecture is not just about designing a facade, but the entire building along with it. The same degree of concern is applied to the fittings and fixtures, right down to the furniture. The furniture and everyday objects in particular should serve the user. Dieter Rams always maintains that design and architecture should be congenial in both attitude and quality.

Jo Klatt
April 1995

目录

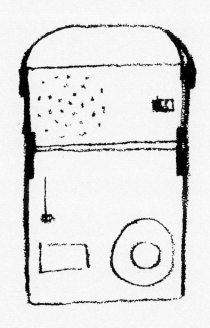

"*TP 1 收音机与唱片机组合一体机*" 的草图

设计的十大原则

　　以下是我为自己及我的同事们所提出的设计哲学，也是关于设计的一些基本考量因素。几年前，我将它们总结为简单的10条原则，希望你也能喜欢。这些原则作为对"好的设计"的指导和理解，经受住了时间的检验。但我们不能也不应该只局限于这10条原则。正如文化和技术是在不断发展一样，对"好的设计"的构成要素的认识也应该是一个不断深入的过程。

好的设计是创新的。

　　好的设计不会复制现有的产品形式，也不会刻意为了创新而创新。相反，"好的设计是创新的"，即它只在明显改进产品功能时才进行创新。设计创新的潜力是无穷的，而技术进步更是在不断地为设计师们的创新方案提供新的机遇。

好的设计是实用的。

　　人们购买产品是为了使用它，因此它必须具有一定的功能，包括主要功能和附加功能。设计最重要的目的就是优化产品的功能实用性。

好的设计是美的。

　　产品的美观度及魅力是其实用性的组成部分。日日夜夜面对着一个令人厌烦的产品是非常令人不快和疲倦的，它会让你感到紧张，根本无法与之相处。然而，关于美观度的讨论一直都是非常困难的，其中的原因主要有2个：一是因为不同的人对词语有不同的理解，所以任何关于视觉方面的描述的讨论都比较困难；二是因为美观度涉及细微的差别和精确的色调，以及各种视觉元素的和谐与微妙平衡。所以，我们必须经过多年实践才能拥有好的鉴赏眼光，从而提出有建设性的意见和建议。

好的设计是使产品易于被理解。

　　好的设计使产品的结构清晰易懂。在某种程度上，好的设计还有助于让产品"说话"。在理想情况下，产品应该是不言自明的，让用户免遭因阅读难以理解的说明书而产生沮丧和乏味感。

Ten Principles of Design

The basic considerations that defined – if you like – a philosophy of design for myself, and my fellow designers, were summed up years ago in the form of ten simple principles. They have stood the test of time as aids to orientation and understanding. They can and should not be binding. Just as culture and technology continue to develop, the idea of what constitutes good design is an evolving process.

Good design is innovative.

It does not copy existing product forms, nor does it create novelty just for the sake of it. Rather, good design is innovative in that it generates innovation only in respect to clear improvements in a product's function. The potential in this respect has by no means been exhausted. Technological progress continues to offer designers new chances for innovative solutions.

Good design makes a product useful.

You buy a product in order to use it. It has to fulfil certain purposes – primary as well as additional functions. The most important responsibility of design is to optimise the utility of a product.

Good design is aesthetic.

The aesthetic quality of a product – and thus its fascination – is an integral aspect of its utility. It is truly unpleasant and tiring to have to put up with products day in and day out that are confusing, that literally get on your nerves, and that you are unable to relate to. However it has always been a hard task to argue about aesthetic quality. For two reasons: First, it is very difficult to discuss anything visual since words have different meanings for different people. Second, aesthetic quality deals with nuances and precise shades, with the harmony and subtle equilibrium of a whole variety of visual elements. You need a good eye trained through years of experience in order to have an informed opinion.

Good design makes a product easy to understand.

It clarifies the structure of a product. It also helps the product speak for itself in a way. Ideally a product should be self-explanatory and save the frustration and tedium of

好的设计是克制的。

功能性产品就像工具一样能够达成某种目的。它们既不是装饰物，也不是艺术品。因此，功能性产品的设计应该是中立的，以使产品低调地保持在背景之中，将表现空间留给用户。

好的设计是诚实的。

好的设计不会试图使产品显得比实际更具创新性、更高效，或者更有用。它绝不试图操纵或欺骗消费者。

好的设计是持久的。

所谓的时髦东西，明天可能就会过时。对于一个被非理性的一次性商品充斥的社会来说，持久性就是设计精良的产品和短命的琐碎物品之间的一个主要区别。

好的设计是彻底的，直到最后的细节。

设计的彻底性和准确性是对产品及其功能的尊重，同时也是对用户的尊重。

好的设计是环保的。

设计必须保持其在保护环境方面的贡献。这不仅包括反对物理方面的环境污染，还包括反对视觉污染和破坏环境。

好的设计就是尽可能少的设计。

回归纯粹，回归简单！

迪特·拉姆斯　1995年

perusing incomprehensible instruction manuals.

Good design is unobtrusive.
Functional products are like tools. They are neither decorative objects nor artworks. Their design should therefore be neutral. They must keep to the background and leave space for the user.

Good design is honest.
It does not attempt to make a product anything other than that which it is – more innovative, more efficient, more useful. It must not manipulate or deceive buyers and users.

Good design is durable.
It has nothing trendy about it that might be out of date tomorrow. This is one of the major differences between well-designed products and short-lived trivial objects for a throwaway society that can no longer be justified.

Good design is thorough, down to the last detail.
Thoroughness and accuracy in design are expressions of respect – for the product and its functions as well as the user.

Good design is environmentally friendly.
Design can and must maintain its contribution towards protecting and sustaining the environment. This does not just include combating physical pollution, but the visual pollution and destruction of our environment as well.

Good design is as little design as possible.
Back to purity, back to simplicity!

Dieter Rams 1995

在博朗的40年

我于1955年夏天入职博朗公司（以下简称博朗），并一直工作到1995年。在设计这个相对年轻的行业里，40年为同一家公司设计产品可以说是很罕见的情况。我和博朗的关系，以及我成为一名设计师，既不是偶然也不是巧合。我作为一名设计师，博朗独特的发展史、理念和事业对我的成长产生了深远影响。我的设计理念是在博朗的框架内形成的，我设计的也主要是博朗的产品。

马克斯·博朗（Max Braun），博朗公司创始人
Max Braun, company founder

让我来简要介绍一下这家公司：博朗公司由工程师马克斯·博朗于1921年在德国的法兰克福创立。马克斯先生是一个精力充沛且富有创造力的人。他具有创新意识，不断地制造出自己构思的新颖产品。在公司早期阶段，他凭借敏锐的商业嗅觉对当时出现的新无线电技术产生了强烈的兴趣，并借此技术获得了成功。博朗公司最初只制造探测器等小部件，但很快就开始生产无线电装置。公司的一个重要技术创新就是制造出了收音机与录音机的组合一体机，这款设备在博朗连续生产了近半个世纪。

博朗公司早期的产品之一——一款探测器，它是早期无线电收音机的核心元件
One of the Braun's early products: a detector, the heart of the early radios

公司成立的早期阶段并不注重外观设计，当时产品的外观是由工程师设计的。这种工程师化的设计往往显得有点笨拙，但绝不是说不好。同时，马克斯·博朗也非常在意其产品的功能形式。

第二次世界大战以前，马克斯·博朗开始研制电动剃须刀。他的儿子欧文·博朗（Erwin Braun）曾写道："他发明了一款风靡很多年的干用剃须刀产品，它带有一个灵活的刀片和可以不断移动的内部刀具。这款产品拥有比当时已知的任何其他剃须刀都突出的优势。"1950年，也就是第一款博朗剃须刀问世后，该公司还推出了自己的第一款家用电器——多功能厨房料理机。

马克斯·博朗于1951年去世。他的2个年轻的儿子阿图尔·博朗（Artur Braun）和欧文·博朗接管了公司，继承了父亲的事业，保留了当时已建立的收音机、唱片机、剃须刀和厨房电器的产品线。同时，他们也走上了一条变革的新路，这条路很

I arrived at Braun in the summer of 1955, and stayed until 1995. Forty years of design for one and the same company is certainly a rare exception in our comparatively young profession. My bond with Braun and the straightness of my path as a designer are neither accidental nor coincidental. The company influenced me strongly as a designer with its special history, with its concepts and with its undertakings. My design ideals were shaped within the framework of Braun and it was Braun products that I primarily designed.

Let me introduce the company with a kind of brief curriculum vitae: Braun was founded in Frankfurt in 1921 by the engineer Max Braun. He was a highly energetic and inventive man with a sense for innovation and consistently manufactured novel products of his own conception. At an early stage he took a keen and successful interest in the new radio technologies that were appearing at the time. Initially Braun manufactured components such as detectors but soon they were producing entire devices. An important innovation was the combination of radio and record player, a type of appliance that Braun then continued to produce for almost half a century.

During this early phase of the company's existence there was no talk of design. The appliances' appearances were shaped by their engineers. This engineered kind of design was often a little clumsy, but by no means bad. Max Braun also took great care to give his products functional forms.

Before World War II, Max Braun started developing an electrically driven shaver. " He invented" , wrote his son Erwin Braun, "what was for years the most used dry shaving system with a flexible blade and constantly moving inner cutters beneath. This system has outstanding advantages over any other system known so far". In 1950, along with the first Braun shaver, the company also launched their first household appliance, the Multimix kitchen machine.

Max Braun died in 1951. His two young sons Artur and Erwin Braun took over the management of the company, continuing their father's work by keeping the hitherto

阿图尔·博朗和欧文·博朗，公司创始人的儿子
Artur and Erwin Braun, sons of the company founder

第一台桌上收音机与唱片机的组合机，机身顶部配有统一的操作控制台
First table radio/phono combination with a unified operating console on the top

快在他们的产品设计和企业交流中变得清晰起来。

1954年，威廉·瓦根菲尔德（Wilhelm Wagenfeld）在达姆施塔特（Darmstadt）举办的一次讲座有力地推动了公司的这一新的设计方向。欧文·博朗后来在《形式》（form）杂志上给瓦根菲尔德的一封信中写道："你曾是我的老师，后来又是我兄弟阿图尔的老师，你是我们'工业设计'的第一位老师。"

请允许我引用威廉·瓦根菲尔德在这场精彩演讲中的几句话：

制造出全面优秀的产品需要聪明的制造商，他们会充分考虑每一件产品的用途、实用性和耐用性。

形式上的探索会引出一系列必须解决的问题，就像化学实验室或医院实验室中的研究任务一样，也需要我们对物质产品有同样的渗透程度，也需要经过无数的研究和测试，以及精心地反复检验和调整，以创造出理性的构造形式。

工业产品越简单，去满足其设计要求就越困难。

早在1954年12月，博朗就与新成立的乌尔姆设计学院（Ulm School of Design）建立了最初的联系。"我从各个渠道获得了有关这个年轻的乌尔姆设计学院的信息，尤其是被我们的无线电木件制造商（他们可能永远不会知道自己在多大程度

established product range: radio and phono sets, shavers and kitchen appliances. But they also simultaneously set out on a revolutionary new path that soon became clear in their product designs and their corporate communications.

A strong impulse for this new design orientation came from a lecture held by Wilhelm Wagenfeld in Darmstadt in 1954. "You were a teacher to me and later to my brother Artur, our first teacher in 'industrial design'", wrote Erwin Braun later in a letter to Wagenfeld published in the magazine "form".

Let me quote a few sentences from this remarkable lecture by Wilhelm Wagenfeld:

"The best by all accounts needs intelligent manufacturers who thoroughly reflect upon the purpose, utility and durability of each and every product."

"Form finding can lead to problems that have to be solved like a research task in a chemist's or physician's laboratory. The same level of penetration into the matter is required, the same searching and probing through endless test series and lastly the equally diligent mental checking and adaptation towards a rational fabrication."

"The simpler an industrial product is supposed to be, the more difficult it is to fulfil the requirements."

As early as December 1954, Braun established first contacts with the newly founded Ulm

博朗生产的第一款电动剃须刀——S 50（1950年）
The first electrical shaver by Braun: S 50 (1950)

博朗的第一代厨房电器
The first Braun kitchen appliance

汉斯·古格洛特（Hans Gugelot, 1920—1965年），乌尔姆设计学院的设计师和教师
Hans Gugelot (1920-1965), designer and teacher at the Ulm School of Design

上加速了木家具时代的终结）多次提起。"（摘自欧文·博朗发表在《形式》杂志上的文章）

汉斯·古格洛特是乌尔姆设计学院的建筑师、设计师和教师，他接受了博朗公司关于收音机和唱片机的设计委托。在奥托·艾舍（Otl Aicher）的监督下，乌尔姆设计学院负责为博朗设计展台和通信设备。乌尔姆设计学院成员、博朗兄弟及弗里茨·艾希勒（Fritz Eichler）博士基于友谊建立了亲密的合作关系。弗里茨·艾希勒是一名戏剧家兼电影导演，他也于1954年（变革之年）加入博朗，加入之初是为了给公司制作广告宣传片。

回顾过去，有4个非常重要的方面决定了博朗的新方向。第一个重要方面，基于一种深刻而严肃的信念，即公司不惜一切代价摒弃对应该如何使自己与众不同的肤浅渴望。恰恰相反，公司想要的是制造出真正有用的、比以往能更好地满足人们需求的产品。

第二个重要方面，变革的新方向是全方位的。它不仅涉及产品设计，还涉及技术、通信、与零售商的合作及公司员工的福利。1954年，博朗建立了自己的医疗保健计划，为员工提供体操锻炼、运动比赛、全食物餐食和桑拿设施等全面的保健服务。公司内部还有一名普通医生和一名牙医。员工可以享受公司的复健设施和物理疗法。物理治疗师兼运动教练沃纳·基

Hochschule für Gestaltung (Ulm School of Design). "The young college, the HfG, was brought to my attention from all sides, in particular by our radio furniture manufacturers who will never know how much they accelerated the end of the wood furniture era." (Erwin Braun in "form" magazine)

Hans Gugelot, an architect, designer and teacher at the HfG, was commissioned to design radio and phono sets. Under the supervision of Otl Aicher, the HfG designed the exhibition stands and corporate communication for Braun. The cooperation between Ulm and the Braun brothers and Dr. Fritz Eichler was a close one, determined by mutual friendship. Fritz Eichler, theatre expert and film director, also came to Braun in 1954, the year of change – initially to produce advertising spots.

In retrospect, four very important aspects determined Braun's new orientation. The first was based on a deep and serious conviction – a desire to avoid, at all costs, a more or less superficial concept of how the company should differentiate itself. They wanted to manufacture products that were genuinely useful and that met people's needs better than before.

The second important aspect, the new orientation, was all embracing. It affected not just product design but also technology, communications, cooperation with retailers and the welfare of the company's own staff.

创新设计：1955年以前的唱片机Phonosuper（右）和1956年的唱片机Phonosuper SK 4（左）
A new kind of design: Phonosuper before 1955 (right) and Phonosuper SK 4 from 1956 (left)

普里安（Werner Kyprian）负责建立并管理这项服务，该项服务的质量和范围在当时都是独一无二的。

不过，第三个重要方面，即对于产品本身的设计才最清晰、最令人信服地展示了博朗公司重新出发的强大势头。这也引出了第4个重要方面——以新设计的产品来开拓公司的新方向，这可谓是一场巨大的商业冒险。时隔近60年后，这一点再怎么强调也不为过。

在60年后的今天，人们已经很难想象这一设计在当时有多么出色，整个公司形象在当时是多么的不凡，更不用说在1955年的柏林国际广播展（Funkausstellong）上以全新的面貌展示公司及其产品系列需要多么大的勇气。对一些同时代的人来说，博朗的这次创新和冒险给他们留下了深刻的印象。他们很快就明白了，这种新的设计远不止是一种新的风格，更是一种电器设计的新尝试，通过使产品的设计形式与功能相一致赋予它们更高的实用价值。

博朗的战略是成功的。虽然这不是一蹴而就的，也不是轻而易举就能获得的成功，但它足够清楚地证明了坚持新道路是正确的。在1957年第11届米兰三年展上，博朗参展的全部产品都赢得了全场大奖（Grand Prix award）。自那以后，新的博朗设计主张开始得到认可。

1957年在柏林举行的国际建筑展上，由世界各地著名建筑师设计的公寓样板间几乎无一例外地都配备了博朗电器。

博朗产品吸引了越来越多的买家。在短短的几年里，不仅收音机和唱片机得到了重新设计，家用电器和剃须刀也得到了重新设计。同时，还有全新开发的一系列产品，如全自动幻灯机PA 1。早在1951年，博朗就建立了一个新的名称为Hobby的照相机闪光灯产品线，格哈德·兰德（Gerhard Lander）博士在其开发过程中发挥了重要作用。

总之，得益于新的设计（当然也不仅仅是因为这一点），博朗公司在10多年间不断发展壮大。公司创造更好产品的努力是全方位的。公司年复一年地推陈出新，

In 1954 Braun established its own health care scheme offering employees a comprehensive health protection programme – through exercise regimes, sports and games, whole foods and a sauna facility. There was a company doctor and a company dentist. Employees could take advantage of remedial gymnastics and physiotherapy. Werner Kyprian, physiotherapist and sport instructor, set up and managed this service, which was unique in terms of both quality and range.

However, a third noteworthy aspect showed the company's redevelopment most clearly and convincingly, and that was the design of the products themselves. And this leads to the fourth aspect which, almost 60 years later, cannot be emphasised more strongly: the new direction with the newly designed products was a huge entrepreneurial risk!

Today, 60 years on, it is hard to imagine how extraordinary this design and the whole company image was back then, and what courage it took to present the company and its product range at the 1955 Funkausstellung [German trade show for radios and home appliances] with a complete and radical new face. For some contemporaries, the novelty and the risk left a very strong impression.

They didn't take long to understand that this new design was far more than just a new 'style' – but an attempt to design appliances that were determined by their function and therefore had a higher intrinsic value.

Braun's strategy was successful. Not all at once, and not without limitations, but clear enough to justify adhering to the new path.

In 1957 Braun's entire programme was awarded the Grand Prix at the 11th Triennale in Milan. The new design requirements began to take hold.

The show apartments at the International Building Exhibition in Berlin in 1957, designed by leading architects from all over the world, were, almost without exception, kitted out with Braun appliances. Braun products attracted more and more buyers. In the course of a few short years, not only were the radio and phono sets redesigned, but also the household appliances and shavers as well. Entirely new products were also added to the

总有新设计的、升级的产品被投放到市场。其中一些产品不仅取得了惊人的成功，还影响了当时的技术发展和其所属类别的市场发展，例如：

Sixtant系列剃须刀、T 1000世界波段收音机、Studio系列模块化高保真系统、KM 3/32厨房料理机、TG 1000磁带录音机、Hobby闪光灯、Nizo S 8 超8摄影机。

当然，也有一些产品由于各种原因而未能占领市场。但它们在商业上的失败很少是因为它们的设计。

博朗的飞速成功也得益于公司股东的支持和贡献。自1967年起，总部位于波士顿的吉列（Gillette）公司便拥有了博朗的大部分股份，并在公司发展方面发挥了主导作用，同时不逼迫博朗违背自己想要成为一家面向世界市场的大型家电制造商的发展意愿。当然，博朗的设计也从未受到过股东的质疑。

如今，博朗的主要产品领域是剃须刀、头发护理用具、家用电器、钟表和口腔护理用具。博朗是这些产品所在的世界市场的重要制造商之一，也是市场领导者。而对于那些博朗并未期望保持领先地位的产品领域，如娱乐电器、电影和摄影产品等，后来就从博朗的产品线中消失了。

range. For example, the fully automatic slide projector PA 1. As early as 1951 Braun established a new product line of flashguns called Hobby, in whose development Dr. Gerhard Lander played a significant role.

For more than a decade Braun grew and expanded, thanks to the new design, but certainly not only because of it. The effort to create better products was all-embracing.

Year by year new, consistently successful products were launched onto the market. Some were sensationally successful and influenced both technological developments at the time and the development of the market in their categories. To name but a few examples:

The sixtant shaver, the T 1000 world receiver, the studio modular hi-fi system, the KM 3/32 kitchen appliances, the TG 1000 tape recorder, the hobby flash guns and the Nizo S 8 super 8 camera.

Naturally there were also products that did not conquer the market for a variety of reasons. But their commercial failure was rarely the result of their design.

Braun also had its shareholders to thank for its rocketing success. As of 1967, the Boston-based company Gillette owned the majority of shares in the company and they played a leading role in dictating the development of the corporation without forcing Braun to be anything other than it wanted to be: a large serial producer of domestic products for the world market. Braun's design was also never questioned.

Today the key product areas are shavers, hair care and household appliances, clocks and oral hygiene appliances. Braun is one of the world's most important manufacturers in these markets and market leader in many countries. The product segments where Braun could never hope to maintain top position, such as entertainment electronics and film and photography products, later disappeared from the range.

"博朗设计之父"
——写在欧文·博朗70岁寿辰之时

The Fathers of Braun Design: To Erwin Braun on his 70th birthday

文章最早发表在《设计＋设计》杂志2004年12月第69/70期，该期杂志是"博朗设计50周年纪念版"专版。

First published in: "Design+Design" Issue No. 69/70, jubilee edition 50 Years of Braun Design, December 2004

亲爱的博朗先生：

Dear Mr Braun,

初次见到您时，您只比我现在的学生们大一点。但是我当时比您年龄小，而您不仅经营着雇佣我的公司，还拥有深远的计划并负责制定决策，所以我在当时与您保持着敬重的距离。坦白说，直到今日我依然如此。

The first time I met you, you were barely older than my students are today. But because I was so much younger myself, because you were running the company that hired me, because you had such far-reaching plans and made the decisions that set so much and so many in motion, I kept a respectful distance back then. And, if I am honest, I still do.

8月是您的70寿辰。自20世纪50年代中期剧烈的动荡岁月，即我们现在所说的"博朗设计"成型时期，一直到现在，大半生都过去了。什么是博朗设计？它的创始人是谁？他对这家公司在产品设计方面的贡献又有哪些呢？

In August you will turn 70. A whole lifetime has passed since those intense years of turmoil in the mid 1950s when what we now so sweepingly call "Braun design" took shape. What is Braun design? Who are its authors? What was your own contribution to the achievements of this company in terms of product design?

实际上，我并不愿意在回顾时把"博朗设计"看作是一个历史性的总结，或准备完结的历史资料。

Actually I am reluctant to look back on "Braun design" as an historic, concluded phenomenon, ripe for the history books.

自1954年以来，为博朗设计的及由博朗自己设计的数百种产品，除了商标之外还有着更多形式上的共同点。它们的诸多相似之处使得谈论"博朗设计"成为可能，而不仅是谈论单个的高保真设备、剃须刀、胶片照相机、厨房用具或吹风机的设计。

It is true that the many hundreds of products that were designed for and by Braun since 1954 have more in common than the brand. They have a similarity, a relationship to one another that makes it possible to talk about "Braun design" rather than just the design of individual hi-fi units, shavers, film cameras, kitchen appliances or hairdryers.

但是，就"博朗设计"而言，它绝不可能被描述为一个简单的初级模板，或是那种可以被机械地应用于越来越多产品的"设计配方"，也不可能被描述为只被一两个发明人拥有的某种技术专利的设计。对我来说，"博朗设计"不是一个设计解决方案，而是一个代表将设计视为挑战的基本态度的术语：始终从一开始就为每种产品寻找一个好的解决方案，并让"好"主要体现在用户的体验上，而不是制造商钱包的体验上。

Nevertheless, and particularly in the case of Braun, it is not possible to describe an initial, simple, specific "design recipe" that was applied mechanically to ever more products. A type of design that could be described like a technical patent and that had just one or two inventors. No, for me "Braun design" is not a solution but a term for a basic attitude that sees design as a challenge: The challenge to always start right at the beginning in the quest for a good solution for each and every product, and to understand "good" primarily as a quality for the user rather than for the manufacturer's wallet.

在我看来，博朗真正的创业成就和设计成就就是实现了这一基本态度并保持了这一态度，而且还以具体的设计形式不断将其付诸实践多年。这是一个有很多人参与的过程，他们在不同时间、以不同角色带来了不同影响。在人类文化史上，有生于无。每一个新事物都有先行者和前导，都需要有适宜的条件才能成长。

多年前，您曾说您的父亲在您之前给博朗提供了重要的推动力，并为即将发生的变革奠定了基础。同时，威廉·瓦根菲尔德显然也发挥了关键作用。您经常提到1954年在达姆施塔特听到他的演讲让您走上了自己的道路。您还经常强调乌尔姆设计学院成员的贡献是多么具有决定性：奥托·艾舍为博朗带来了概念上的启发，而汉斯·古格洛特作为一名建筑师和设计师，更是遵循新的、面向用户和功能的方法成功设计了第一批博朗产品。

弗里茨·艾希勒以完全不同的角色和影响参与了"博朗设计"的开发。他有时喜欢说自己是一名"助产士"，是提供灵感、支持和鼓励的对话伙伴。此外，与瓦根菲尔德和古格洛特一起及在他们之后设计电器的其他10余位设计师——从赫伯特·赫什（Herbert Hirche）到1990年、1991年加入设计部门的年轻同事，每一位设计师在整个成就中都发挥了自己的独特作用。

留心观察的人可能会注意到这里竟没有您的名字！事实也的确如此，在回顾博朗公司异军突起和迅速发展的过程时，您所扮演的角色常常被一笔带过。这也符合您谦虚的品质。当我说您在整个过程中扮演着至关重要的角色时，这并不是对生日男孩的赞美，而是在试着做出一种更符合现实的描述。

您的角色是非常关键的。若是没有您，其他参与者都将无法发挥出现有的影响力，更不用说他们一起协作的效果了。

The true entrepreneurial and design achievement in my view is to have reached this basic attitude and then to have maintained it and put it into practice over and over again in the form of concrete designs for so many years. This was a process that many people were involved in, at different times, in a variety of roles and to varying effect. In the history of human culture, nothing comes from nothing. Every new thing has forerunners and precursors and needs beneficial conditions in which to grow.

Years ago, you stated that your father before you provided important impulses and laid the foundations for what was to come. Wilhelm Wagenfeld also clearly played a key role. You often talked about his lecture you heard in Darmstadt in 1954 that set you on your path. You have also often underlined how decisive the contributions of the Ulmers were – those of Otl Aicher, which were conceptually inspiring and of Hans Gugelot who, as an architect and designer, designed the first successful Braun products that followed the new, user-and function-oriented approach.

Fritz Eichler was involved in the development of Braun design in a completely different role and with a different kind of impact. He sometimes enjoyed saying that he acted as the "midwife"; as a dialogue partner who provided inspiration, support and encouragement. Also the ten or so other designers who designed appliances both with and after Wagenfeld and Gugelot – from Herbert Hirche to the younger colleagues who joined the design department in 1990 and 1991, each had his or her own specific part to play in this whole achievement.

An alert observer will have noticed that one name is missing here – yours! And it is true that your role in the retrospective accounts of the emergence and development of Braun is often far too briefly mentioned. This matches your own tendency to underplay your own achievements. When I say that I believe you were crucial to the whole thing, it is not meant as just praise for the birthday boy, but as an attempt at a more realistic account.

Your role was key in that not a single one of the other participants could have been as effective in the same way without you, not to mention all of them together in collaboration.

瓦根菲尔德当时的讲座有许多其他企业家在场，他甚至还和他们中的一些人一起工作了很长时间。可是，这些公司重要的、耐久的、生动的设计成就现在又在哪里呢？真正让瓦根菲尔德变得如此有影响力的正是1954年的一位年轻商人。这位年轻人坐在那间礼堂里聆听了他的建议，并且切实采纳了这些建议。

所有为博朗工作、与博朗合作的支持者及理念一致的人和设计师，当然也包括我，都对制造质量不同寻常的产品、不同寻常的产品设计、不同寻常的公司发展有着远见卓识。您专门进行了深入调研，寻找能够实现自己愿景的人。您将自己的想法传达给设计师，激励他们，赋予他们想象空间，并推动他们不断地对设计结果进行反复且细致的评估。他们也带着极大的热情为建设性的、以设计为主导的产品创新奠定了基础。他们冒着巨大的风险，坚持不懈地将不同寻常（这些产品的设计角度显然也是不同寻常的）的产品推向市场。他们坚持走自己的道路。

安东尼奥·西特里奥（Antonio Citterio）在写给维特拉（Vitra）公司的罗尔夫·菲尔巴姆（Rolf Fehlbaum）的信中提到："作为一名设计师，我坚信客户的绝对重要性，无论就其职责地位还是就其个人方面而言都是如此。所有的建筑或产品都有一位'母亲'和一位'父亲'——建筑师（或设计师）和客户。"

为什么很多公司的设计无论是在当时还是现在都是一场悲剧？毫无疑问，好的设计在商业上也应该是成功的。维特拉公司和欧科（Erco）公司就是好的设计的经典例子。很多公司都有机会在这方面有所作为。当前的市场上有很多好的理念和初期探索，但也有同样多的因犹豫退缩而导致的失败、平庸和困惑。不管是在1954年还是在1991年，即使是稍微了解现实的设计师也会知道决定性因素是公司管理层的洞察力、态度、能力和具体表现。

遗憾的是，公司管理层的经理们通常只准备发布几条含糊不清、抽象的意向声明，大致意思就是"我们会为产品的卓越设计而努力"。这类声明的微弱效果几乎和蝴蝶扇动几下翅膀差不多。您的言谈举

What Wagenfeld said back then could have been heard by plenty of other entrepreneurs. He even worked long and intensively with some of them. But where are the important, enduring, lively design achievements of these companies today? What made Wagenfeld so influential in 1954 was the young businessman who sat in the auditorium, absorbed his suggestions, and then actually went and implemented them.

The same holds true for all the other inspirers, co-thinkers and designers that worked for and with Braun – including myself, of course. They had a vision of different products of a different quality, of another kind of product design, of another kind of company. They searched specifically and intensively for people who were able to realise their vision. They communicated their ideas to their designers; they motivated them, gave them space and constantly re-evaluated the resulting designs in great detail. They laid the foundations for constructive, design-led innovation with élan. They took great risks and persevered to bring products to the market that were different from all the rest, and moreover, that had been designed from a clearly different perspective. They stuck to their course with great tenacity.

Antonio Citterio wrote to Rolf Fehlbaum of Vitra: " As a designer I am convinced of the fundamental importance of the client, in terms of both his function and his person. All architecture and all products have a mother and a father: the architect or designer and his client".

Why is the design of so many companies, then as now, such a tragedy? It must be obvious by now that good design is also commercially successful. Vitra and Erco have also become good examples of that. So many companies had and have the chance to be capable in this respect. There are so many good intentions and initial efforts and there is just as much fainthearted and inconsequential failure, mediocrity and confusion. A designer that knows the reality knows, too, where the deciding factor lies, be it 1954 or 1991: it lies with the company management, their insight, their attitude, their abilities and their concrete achievements.

止则向我们清楚地展示了好的设计需要公司管理层做出何种程度的努力。而且，您的参与程度是完全不同寻常的。如果在众多主角中挑选一位"博朗设计之父"，那么只有您可以配得上这个名号。

但是，正如这世界一样，孩子们长大后会充满敬意地与父亲分离，因为他们要自力更生，并为这世界带来一些新的东西。

Handing out a couple of vague and abstract statements of intent from the executive along the lines of " we aspire to excellent design with our products" is still, sadly, just about all that company managers are generally prepared to do for design. It is about as effective as the flap of a butterfly's wing. Your example shows us exactly what kind of company effort is required. Your involvement was of a fundamentally different kind. If any of the many protagonists can be rightly called the "father of Braun design" then you can.

But – as it goes in the world – the children grow up and they detach themselves respectfully from their fathers because they must, and will, make their own way and bring new things to it.

在博朗的早期阶段

1979年，迪特·拉姆斯给欧文·博朗写了一封公开信，介绍自己早年在博朗担任设计师的情况。欧文·博朗当时住在瑞士，他和他的兄弟阿图尔在1951—1967年担任博朗公司的联合首席执行官。欧文于1992年去世。这封信发表于1989年的《若阿内斯·波坦特，布拉克尔，50年代的设计》（ *Johannes Potente, Brakel , Design der 50er Jahre* ）[1]一书中，这是一本关于设计师若阿内斯·波坦特的书。

亲爱的博朗先生：

这是我在博朗早期职业生涯的回忆录，比承诺交给您的时间晚了一点。

为了让人们更好地了解我的个人发展，我不得不写得更详细一些，希望您能理解。

我坚信自己对设计的态度和兴趣受到了祖父的强烈影响，他是一位出色的木匠。在我十二三岁的时候，我经常待在他的工作室里。

我的祖父没有机器，也不喜欢机器。而且，因为学徒们做事总是做得不够好，所以他更喜欢一个人工作。

他专门从事打磨家具表面的工作，我从他那里学到了如何一层一层地手工打磨木材。

他时不时会做些小家具。他先仔细地从木材商那里挑选一些木材，然后把它们手工打磨成形。通过这种方式制作的简单实用的物品会以一种完全自然的方式呈现，而不是时髦的"盖尔森基兴–巴洛克"（Gelsenkirchen Baroque）风格。这些小家具的设计也反映了他工作方式的经济性，即只需要用手工就可以制作完成。

当然，当时我并没有意识到这些。但我接受了这种设计理念，直至今天我都在关注着设计的朴素和简单。从我记事起，这就是我想要的东西。此外，我在祖父的工作室里还发现了几本来自德国赫勒劳工坊（Deutsche Werkstätten）的产品目录，它们令我印象深刻。

The Early Years at Braun

In 1979 Dieter Rams wrote an open letter to Erwin Braun in which he gave an account of his early years as a designer at Braun. Erwin Braun, who, together with his brother Artur, was the company's joint CEO from 1951 to 1967, was living in Switzerland at the time. He died in 1992. The letter was published in 1989 in " Johannes Potente, Brakel, Design der 50er Jahre" [1] a book about the designer Johannes Potente.

Dear Mr Braun,

Here, a little later than promised, are my memoirs of my early professional life at Braun.

In order to get a better view of my personal development, I was obliged to write in somewhat more detail, I hope you will understand.

I believe that my attitude and my interests were strongly influenced by my grandfather, who was a master joiner. At the age of 12 or 13 I was often to be found in his workshop.

My grandfather had no machines, he didn't like them, and he preferred to work alone; apprentices never did things well enough.

He specialised in surfaces and I learned from him how to polish wood by hand, layer by layer.

Now and then he made small, one-off pieces of furniture. The wood for these he carefully chose from the timber merchant, then edged and planed it into shape by hand. The resulting simple and utilitarian pieces came into being in a totally natural way – no 'Gelsenkirchen Baroque'. Their design reflected the economy of his way of working, they grew out of his handcraft.

Of course I was not aware of this at the time. But I absorbed it and it has been part of me to this day. I have always been concerned with the plain and the simple. For as long as I can remember, this is what I have wanted. In my grandfather's workshop I also found several catalogues from the Deutsche Werkstätten (" German Workshops") that had a great impression on me.

因此，我很自然地就接受了关于创意专业的职业技术培训。1947年，在我年纪还不大的时候，我就开始在威斯巴登（Wiesbaden）的工艺美术学校（Kunstgewerbeschule）学习了，当时该学校刚刚重新开放。我学的专业是室内设计。2个学期后，我中断了学业并在一家木匠作坊当了3年学徒。

这家作坊已经初具工业规模，因此，如果我想学习手工技能就必须另谋去处。幸运的是我能够运用从祖父那里学到的东西。这可能就是我当时能够凭借自己的熟练手工赢得地区奖的原因。当我重回学校时，学校已经发生了新的变化——改名为应用艺术学校（Werkkunst schulen）。后来，我下定决心回到威斯巴登。那里的索德（Söder）教授对我影响很大，他是应用艺术学校的联合创始人之一。如果当初他被批准自由研发，那么后来发生在乌尔姆设计学院的事情很可能首先就发生在威斯巴登了。但索德教授一直未能实施他的计划，并且还因此引起一系列事件。我仍然记得我们还组织了学生示威活动（在当时是相当罕见的），以抗议地方和地区资助政策的短视。

那时，我开始逐渐专注于建筑设计。索德教授是一名建筑师，他在室内设计和空间与设备设计科室的旁边设立了一个建筑科室。他对建筑和设计之间的联系非常感兴趣。

雨果·库克豪斯（Hugo Kükelhaus）和汉斯·哈芬里希特（Hans Haffenrichter）教授当时是学校的客座讲师，他们的一些讲座给我留下了深刻印象。总的来说，这是一个富有成效的时期。由于战争的原因，许多学生的年龄比我大得多，而我有幸成为其中最年轻的一员。

最终，我以优异的成绩毕业，并成为一名室内设计师。接着，我成为大街上的闲人，1953年的经济衰退令建筑设计停滞不前。对更优秀的、更有洞察力的建筑师而言，那种忙碌的建筑热潮——我想要的光景还未到来。

It stood to reason that I would train in a creative profession. At an early age, in 1947, I began studying at the Kunstgewerbeschule (School of Arts and Crafts) in Wiesbaden that had just reopened. My discipline was interior design. After two semesters I interrupted my studies with a three-year apprenticeship in a carpenters' workshop.

This company worked on a fairly industrial scale. If I wanted to learn handcraft skills, I had to find them out myself. Luckily I was able to draw on what I had learned from my grandfather. That may have been the reason why I won a regional prize with my final journeyman's piece. By the time I returned to my studies, the colleges had been through further changes. They were then called Werkkunstschulen (Schools of Applied Arts). I made a conscious decision to return to Wiesbaden. There was a teacher there who influenced me a lot, Professor Dr. Dr. Söder. He was one of the co-founders of the Werkkunstschule concept. If this man had been allowed free rein, what later happened at Ulm would most likely have happened in Wiesbaden first. But Söder was not able to realise his agenda and drew the resulting consequences. I can still remember the student demonstration (quite rare in those days) that we organised in protest against the short-sightedness of local and regional funding policies.

Back then I began to concentrate more and more on architecture. Söder was an architect by profession and had set up an architecture department alongside the department for "interior design and design for space and appliances". He was very interested in the connection between architecture and design.

Hugo Kückelhaus and Professor [Hans] Haffenrichter were guest lecturers back then. Some of their lectures left lasting impressions on me. On the whole it was a very fruitful time. Because of the war, many of the students were far older than I was, and I was fortunate enough to be the youngest.

I graduated in the end as an interior designer – with distinction. Then I found myself out on the street for the first time – literally. In1953 there was a recession. Nothing much was happening in architecture. The hectic building boom times had not yet reached the better,

于是，我找到了一份景观设计师的临时工作，但很快就跳槽了。因为我想成为一名建筑师，而不是一名室内设计师。

如果可能的话，我当时希望能回到大学继续深造，因为我对城市规划（现在的环境设计）特别感兴趣。但是，我需要钱，因为之前自己一直都是勤工俭学。在我对自己感兴趣的建筑师职位投递了职位申请书之后，我便带着作品资料和学位证书拜访了法兰克福的所有建筑工作室和事务所。这就是我走进海因里希·特森诺（Heinrich Tessenow）的前学生奥托·阿佩尔（Otto Apel）的事务所的原因。想到自己当时羞怯的性格，我至今仍然觉得自己非常不可思议。阿佩尔翻阅了我的资料，并问了我一些问题，如你是做什么的？你做过什么项目？你的父亲是谁？等等。然后他就当场决定雇用了我。

我会经常想起自己在阿佩尔的事务所度过的那两年。对我来说，那是决定性的重要时期。在那里，我能够按照自己的方式工作，也能够增加对大型建筑施工的知识。阿佩尔事务所与SOM建筑师事务所（Skidmore, Owings and Merrill office）的合作令我印象深刻，且对我影响深远，当时二者的合作才刚刚开始。我坚信正是这次合作使我能够从容应对以后在博朗工业设计中所遇到的问题，因为SOM团队教给阿佩尔的首席建筑师们［全都是建筑师埃贡·艾尔曼（Egon Eiermann）的崇拜者］的都是工业建筑的经典范例。我记得他们是如何以1∶1的比例建造美国驻法兰克福领事馆的各个部分的，并用于研究和解决所有细节问题。我很少经历像建那3座美国领事馆建筑那样顺利而高效的建设过程。

那么，我为什么会去了博朗呢？起初，这纯粹是个偶然。我办公室里的一位同事发现了一则广告，我猜想大概是发表在《法兰克福评论报》（Frankfurter Rundschau）上面的，写着当时的博朗广播公司（Radio Braun）正在招聘建筑师。

我当时根本没听说过博朗公司，但还是和同事一起提交了职位申请。这

more discerning architects, and that is where I wanted to be. I took a temporary job with a rural architect but skipped out pretty quickly. I wanted to work as an architect – not as an interior designer.

If it had been possible, I would have liked to go back to college at some point. I was particularly interested in urban planning, or environmental design as it is called today. But I needed money. I had already financed my studies myself to a large extent. After I had written my fingers raw for a while with applications to architects that I found interesting, I tucked my portfolio and my degree project under my arm and went around to all the Frankfurt architecture offices in person. That is how I came to walk into the office of the former Tessenow student Otto Apel – which considering my shyness back then still seems pretty incredible to me. He leafed through my portfolio whilst firing questions at me like: What are you? What have you done? Who is your father? And then hired me on the spot.

I often think about the two years I spent at the Apel office. They were decisively important times for me. I was able to work there just as I had imagined I would and was also able to expand my knowledge of the construction of large buildings. I must not forget to mention the influence that Apel's collaboration with the Skidmore, Owings and Merrill office had at the time either, which had just started back then. I believe that this provided the foundation for my ability to deal with what I later encountered in industrial design at Braun, since the things that the Skidmore team taught the then-chief architects at Apel (all Eiermann enthusiasts) constituted an exemplary education in industrial building. I remember how they built sections of the American consulate on a 1∶1 scale in order to study and solve all the detailing. I have seldom experienced such a smooth and efficient construction process as that of those three American consulates back then.

How did I end up at Braun? At first it was purely by accident. A colleague at the office found an advertisement – I think it was in the Frankfurter Rundschau – for a job as an architect at Radio Braun, as it was called then.

I didn't know Braun at all, but applied nevertheless, along with my colleague. It was a

更像是一次打赌，我们想看看谁会得到回应。

结果，我是那个得到回应的人。然而，回应来得太晚了，以至于我都忘记曾申请过。我被邀请到拉塞尔海默大街（Russelsheimer Straβe）来找格罗曼（Grohmann）夫人。如果我没记错的话，亲爱的博朗先生，我当时曾在门厅碰到了您。我没想到那个一开始和我聊天的友好年轻人就是这家公司的老板，直至我们的谈话进行了一段时间后，我才恍然大悟。我记得您简单地看了一下我带来的作品，然后告诉我您收到了好几份申请，并决定给每个人布置一份测试任务——设计一套房间供客人住宿。突然，这让我对所有事情都更加感兴趣了。当您开始告诉我您的计划和想法，并向我展示一些产品时，它就变得更加有趣了。它们一定是在1955年柏林国际广播展上展出的那些产品原型。当时，我被古格洛特的设计深深震撼了，就像在我之后参观过这些产品的许多其他建筑师一样。

那时候，我的工作和产品设计一点儿关系也没有。我的任务是与博朗的房屋建筑师（我已记不清他的名字）合作实施各种建筑项目。所以，我完成了测试任务之后就把它发给了博朗。同样，也是过了一段时间之后我才收到了答复，但是我根本没有在意。事实上，当时我对自己在阿佩尔事务所的工作非常满意。1955年7月，我再一次收到了工作邀请，是您给了我这份工作。

我提交的测试答卷一定是起到了关键作用，因为过了很久以后，汉斯·古格洛特告诉我当时曾有人向他征求意见，他投了我的票。

我必须承认，在最初的两三个月里，我对像博朗这样的公司是如何运作的并不清楚。起初，我和负责设计宣传册及广告的平面设计师（当时他们也是被这样称呼的）在同一间办公室。他们享有一定程度的自由去做自己想做的事情（并且利用了这一点），这给我的印象是他们并不十分辛苦。但这种情况即将发生改变。当时，我还帮助摄影师们在合适的

sort of bet as to who of us would get a response.

I was the one who got an answer. However it arrived so much later that I had forgotten I had even applied. I was invited to come to Rüsselsheimer Straße and to ask for Mrs Grohmann. If I remember correctly, I bumped into you then, dear Mr Braun, in the foyer. It didn't occur to me that the friendly young man who started chatting to me could be the boss of the company. It was a while into the conversation before the penny dropped. I recall you looking briefly at the work that I had brought with me and then telling me that you had had several applications for the post and decided to give everyone a test assignment. The task was to design a set of rooms to be used as guest accommodation. Suddenly this made everything a whole lot more interesting for me. It became even more interesting when you began to tell me about your plans and ideas and to show me a few things. It must have been the prototypes for the products that were to be shown at the Funkausstellung in 1955. I was enraptured by Gugelot's designs – as were many other architects after me.

There was no hint of any connection between me and design at that point. My task would be to collaborate with the Braun house architect (whose name I can no longer remember) on various architectural projects. So I completed the test assignment and sent it off to Braun. It was once again a while before I received a reply. But I didn't mind at all. I was actually totally happy and content with my work at Apel. It must have been in July 1955 before I was invited over again, and you offered me the job.

My test design must have been what clinched it for me. A long time afterwards, Hans Gugelot told me that he had been asked for an opinion and that he had voted for me.

I have to confess that for the first two or three months I was, and remained, pretty unclear about how a company like Braun functioned. In the beginning I sat in the same room as the graphic designers (as they were still called then) who designed the brochures and advertisements. They enjoyed a certain amount of freedom to do whatever they wanted (and took advantage of it) and I had the impression that they were not exactly overworked. But that was about to change.

环境下拍摄新产品。有件事也许您还记得，我当时设法使您与我的一位前同学取得了联系，他刚刚开设了一家诺尔（Knoll）设计公司的代理机构。虽然我的职位和确切的工作范畴还不明确，但您总是确保让我能够处理一些有趣的项目。例如，一个附属于正在翻新的卫生中心的展馆项目，以及您在柯尼希施泰因（Königstein）的建筑项目（后来由汉斯·古格洛特接手）。我保留了自己当时的设计，并且最近又重新翻看了一遍。我必须得说它们可一点儿也不赖。

《明镜周刊》（Der Spiegel）杂志曾报道说，我早期在博朗只被允许整理桌子。这是《明镜周刊》典型的夸张写作手法，我也向其抗议过这一点。事实上，我的时间被一大堆小而无害的（但很重要！）室内设计任务占满了。正因为如此，我才有机会接触公司里的很多人，并越来越了解博朗是怎样的、博朗想要成为一家什么样的公司，了解到您和汉斯·古格洛特、赫伯特·赫什、弗里茨·艾希勒之间的对话及由此产生的新想法，当然还有您的热情。说实话，只是与您的谈话就让我感到获益良多。我深知您的愿景和计划所覆盖的范围是非常广泛的，绝不仅仅局限于产品，还包括了社区健康、营养，以及工作场所和整个生活区的设计。它们都源于同一个核心理念、同一个核心立场，而这个愿景对我而言也渐渐变得可以想象和具体化了。

那时候，我与外部的联系是怎样的呢？我当然听说过乌尔姆设计学院，但当时我与它没有任何联系。我也知道艾希勒博士，但在最初的几个月里，我与他也几乎没有联系。

我在产品设计方面最早的贡献之一就是为博朗带来了我以前的同学。当时，我已经认识了您的兄弟阿图尔，他询问我是否认识懂得如何使用石膏的人，这可能与厨房用具的新设计有关。之前负责此事的人（显然是某个原型设计师）刚刚离开了博朗，于是我推荐了格德A. 穆勒（Gerd A. Müller）。他是1955年12月第一批来到博朗的人之一，在当时的第

I helped out the photographers who were tasked with the job of photographing the new products in a suitable environment. Perhaps you still remember this problem? I managed to put you in touch with a former fellow student of mine who had just opened an agency for Knoll. My own position and exact job description were still unclear, but nevertheless you always made sure that I got interesting projects to deal with. For example, an exhibition pavilion that was to be attached to the refurbished health centre. Or your own building project in Königstein, which was later taken over by Hans Gugelot. I kept my designs from back then and looked at them again recently. I must say they were not that bad.

"Der Spiegel" once wrote that I was only allowed to straighten up the desks during my early career at Braun. That is a typical Spiegel statement, and I said so. In reality I was occupied with a whole load of small, harmless (but important!) interior design tasks. I came into contact with a lot of people in the company as a result and learned more and more about what Braun was. About what Braun wanted to be – about the conversations between yourself and Hans Gugelot, Herbert Hirche and Fritz Eichler, about ideas that were born then and your enthusiasm – I learned only from conversations with you. I understood that your vision and your plans were very broadly based and not at all restricted to just products. The realisation that community health, nutrition, designs for the workplace and the design of entire living areas could come from a single core idea, a single position, became conceivable and tangible.

What about my external contacts at that time? I had heard of Ulm of course, but didn't have anything to do with them at that point. I knew about Dr. Eichler too, but had little contact with him in these early months.

One of my very first achievements in product design was that I was able to bring a former fellow student to Braun. I had got to know your brother Artur, who asked me if I knew anyone who understood how to work with plaster. It was to do with the new design of a kitchen appliance. The person that was previously responsible for it (apparently some kind of prototype designer) had just

一工厂与技术人员共事，并开始从事石膏模型工作。

大约在同一时期，您让我与WK协会（WK-Verband）合作设计一款新产品来替代古格洛特设计的家电，以便与诺尔公司的家具更搭配。此外，您还让我负责改良木制收音机和唱片机柜。

因此，我又开始用到我最初使用的材料——木材。但此时我已经不再喜欢它了，我认为木材不是制作收音机外壳的合适材料。

我隐约记得自己当时尝试使用一种替代性的金属板材质的收音机机箱，而非当时其他电器通常使用的那种外壳。但是，我没有取得成果。我对收音机和唱片机柜也没有做大的改动，对WK产品也一样，尽管它最终投产了。

在博朗工作的最初几个月里，我还参与制订了SK1收音机和SK2收音机早期的色彩方案，以及对exporter便携式收音机的改进（即我们现在俗称的重新设计）。

那时我有很多事情要做，并且被批准可以找个人来帮我。于是，1956年3月罗兰·魏根德（Roland Weigend）加入了我们。他在博朗产品设计公司担任了多年的模型车间主任。那时，我已经和技术人员建立了更密切的联系，并有了自己的办公室。不久之后，魏根德、我和格德 A. 穆勒共同拥有了一间更大的新工作室，我们在那里还安装了自己的模型制作设备。不过，这间工作室仍然很简陋：一个工作台、一块绘图板、一台车床，以及之前提到的石膏，除此之外再没有其他东西了。就这样，我们自己所谓的设计（Formgestaltung）部门诞生了。

我与一台D 50投影仪模型机的合影（1959年）
Myself with a model of the projector D 50(1959)

left Braun. I recommended Gerd A. Müller, who was one of the first to come to Braun in December 1955 and literally took up, in the (then) Factory 1, direct contact with the technicians and started to work in plaster.

Around the same time, you asked me to design a new product in collaboration with the WK-Verband as an alternative to the Gugelot appliances that were designed to go more with the Knoll furniture. You also asked me to take care of alterations in the wooden radio and phono cabinets.

So there I was back with the material that I had started with – wood. But I didn't like it anymore. I didn't believe that wood was the right material for a radio casing.

I seem to recall that I started experimenting with a sheet metal alternative for a radio chassis instead that was being used in almost all the other appliances at the time. Not a lot came of it. Not a lot came of the alterations to the radio and phono cabinets either, or the WK appliance – although it eventually went into production.

In the first few months of my employment I was also involved in colour prototypes for the SK 1 and 2 and in changes (what we would now call redesign) to the exporter.

By then I had a lot to do and was allowed to look for someone to help me. In March 1956, Roland Weigend joined us. He went on to work for many years as head of the model workshop at Braun product design. I had established closer ties with the technicians by that time and had been given my own room. Shortly afterwards, Weigend, myself and Gerd A. Müller were given a new, larger room together where we also installed our own model building equipment. It was still very modest: a joiner's bench, a drawing board, a lathe and not much else apart from the previously mentioned plaster. And so the Formgestaltung (as we called design back then) department was born.

无线电设备
Radio

1956—1957年　SK 4唱片机与收音机组合一体机
1956/1957　SK 4

　　　　transistor 1 便携式收音机
　　　　transistor 1

　　　　Phonokoffer PC 3 便携式唱片机
　　　　Portable phono PC 3

1957年　atelier 1 立体声音响系统
1957　atelier 1
　　　　立体声音响系统的早期产品，配有两
　　　　个独立的L 1扬声器
　　　　Forerunner to stereophonic system
　　　　with two separate loudspeakers L1
　　　　L 1扬声器也适合作为SK 4组合一体
　　　　机的附属扬声器
　　　　Also suitable as additional loudspeakers
　　　　for the SK 4

1958—1959年　Studio 2 模块化高保真音响系
　　　　　　　统第一款模块化/组件高保真
　　　　　　　音响系统
1958/59　Studio 2
　　　　LE 1静电扬声器，以及适合于
　　　　atelier 1 立体声音响系统的L 2
　　　　扬声器
　　　　First modular/component hi-fi
　　　　system. Electrostatic loudspea-
　　　　kers LE 1 and (for the atelier) the
　　　　loudspeaker L 2

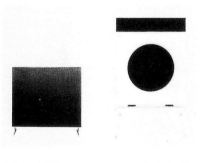

1959年　集成了T 4晶体管收音机的TP 1组合一
　　　　体机
1959　Phono combination TP 1
　　　　with transistor receiver T4
1959年　T 41晶体管收音机
1959　Transistor receiver T 41
1960年　T 52晶体管收音机
1960　Transistor receiver T 52

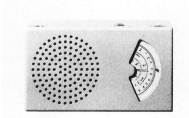

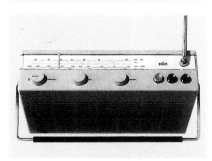

家用电器
Household
1956—1957年 KM 3厨房料理机
1956/57 Kitchen machine KM 3
1957—1958年 Multimix MX 3多功能搅拌机和
Multipress MP 3多功能榨汁机
1957/58 Multimix MX 3 and Multipress MP 3
1960年 M 121搅拌器
1960 Mixer M 121

剃须刀
Shaver
1956—1957年 Combi电动剃须刀（设计修订版）
1956/57 Combi (revised design)
1959—1960年 SM 3电动剃须刀
1959/60 Shaver SM 3

摄像类设备
Photo
1956年 PA 1全自动幻灯机
1956 Fully automatic slide projector PA 1
1958年 Hobby Special EF 2 照相机闪光灯
1958 Hobby Special EF 2
1959年 Hobby F 60照相机闪光灯
1959 Hobby F 60

风扇型暖风机
Fan Heater
1959年 与莱因·埃克（Laiing-Eck）合作：
第一台小型紧凑型暖风机，配有H 1切
向鼓风机
1959 In collaboration with Laiing-Eck:
The first small and compact heater
with tangential blower H 1

正是在这样的环境条件下，我全程参与设计的第一台设备——SK4组合一体机诞生了，它也被称作"白雪公主的棺木"。这也是我第一次与乌尔姆设计学院、汉斯·古格洛特的直接合作。

弗里茨·艾希勒曾说："拉姆斯和我被难住了。"那时我还太年轻，甚至没有意识到一个人会被难住，我也不想承认这一点。但我们确实未能以正确的方式阐述我们的想法。在这方面，我们有很多东西要学。在这个时期，乌尔姆设计学院、汉斯·古格洛特团队，以及博朗这些"年轻人"之间的合作对我的影响是最大的。

当收音机与唱片机组合一体机设计最终完成时（我们最终为它设计了一个有机玻璃盖，它的绰号就是因这个盖子得来的。若是没有它，就没有今天的唱片机），我真的非常高兴。我们通过专门为它设计的部分金属外壳和机箱而实现了一个创新概念，并影响了整整一代电器的设计。在那个年代，产品设计师的名字仍然会在产品发布时被提及，因此大家都确保要让我的名字也被提及。每当想到这一点，我都心怀感激。

我经常被问到，博朗的设计师是如何打造出自己的权威，并取代了乌尔姆设计团队的设计师，直到最终所有设计都由博朗内部设计部门负责。我想说这是一个完全自然的过程。当我刚开始在博朗工作时，乌尔姆设计团队很自然地占据了主导地位。当时，博朗与他们的合作已经开展了一段时间，我在其中参与得不太多。有时候，乌尔姆设计团队会来到博朗，和您、艾希勒博士及阿图尔·博朗进行交流。有时候，您会开车去乌尔姆设计学院，让学院的人给您提供设计建议。但与此同时，我也在一步步地投入工作，我只是碰巧拥有了在公司内部工作的先天优势。

在博朗从事建筑工作让我有机会与很多人建立了良好的关系。接着，在博朗参与产品设计之初，技术方面毋庸置疑是极其重要的，所以可以说我碰巧又占了技术方面的上风。尽管我当时的收入仍然很低，但我还是买了几瓶杜松子

This was the environment in which the first appliance with which I was involved right from the beginning took shape. It was the SK 4, or ' Snow White's coffin'. Here too came my first direct collaboration with Ulm in the shape of Hans Gugelot.

Fritz Eichler once put it like this: " Rams and I got stuck". I was too young back then to even realise that one can get stuck. I refused to believe it. But it is true that we were not able to interpret our ideas in the right way. We had a lot to learn in this respect. This was the moment at which the collaboration that had developed between Ulm, Hans Gugelot and his people and us 'young ones' had the greatest influence on me.

When the radio/audio combination was finally finished (right at the end it acquired the Plexiglas lid that gave it its nickname and without which any record player is now unimaginable), I was really happy. With the partly metal housing and the specially developed chassis we had realised a concept that was to influence a whole new generation of appliances. In those days the product designers were still mentioned by name and they made sure that I was named as well – which is something that I recall with gratitude.

I am often asked how we Braun designers managed to create our own degree of authority and "supercede" the Ulmers until finally all design was taken care of by the Braun internal design department. It was a totally organic process. When I started at Braun, the Ulmers dominated, naturally. The collaboration with them had been going on for some time. I wasn't involved that much. The Ulm designers came and dealt with you, Dr. Eichler and Artur Braun. Or you drove there and let them advise you. But at the same time, the workload was steadily increasing. I just happened to have the advantage of being in-house.

Through my architecture jobs at Braun I had already made a number of good contacts. Then, as it became clear, right at the beginning of product design at Braun, how important the technical side of things was, you could say that I happened to have the upper hand. (Admittedly it did cost me a few bottles of schnapps, despite my still very modest income, to develop a good working

酒来与一些更难相处的技术人员建立良好的工作关系。我觉得当时向技术人员明确表示我们不想剥夺他们的工作，而是要支持他们是非常必要的。尽管我懂得相关技术并有建筑教育背景，我自己也不是外行，但我仍然有很多东西要向他们学习。

当然，当产品出现紧急问题时，技术人员可以更容易找到我也是一个优势。我可以和他们一起研究绘图板上的设计方案，因此我也能比任何外部设计师更快、更好地找到解决方法，直至今日我也是这样认为的。

这种形式的团队合作依赖于人们达成共识。艾希勒博士也一直强调这一点。然而，只有当你能够真正理解他人的工作、尊重他们的成就，并不断地重新审视他们的利益时，才能够实现这一目标。我与许多技术人员的密切关系就是在那时发展起来的，有些人还成了我的好朋友。我认为，即使在今天，博朗仍然在从这种良好的员工关系中受益。若没有这种良好的关系氛围，你甚至无法做出像样的设计。无论你的营销方案有多么完美，它都是无可取代的。

我们这个年轻部门内部的职责分工仍然没有明确界定。最终是格德·A.穆勒负责设计家用电器，包括剃须刀，我负责设计闪光灯、新的幻灯机和收音机，而罗兰·魏根德是一位无所不能的通才，他制作了第一批产品模型，同时还按照比例尺绘制了相应的印刷模板。

我们在1960年之前的几年所开发的新产品模型会在后面陆续展示。

赫伯特·赫什第一次知道我的名字最有可能是在我研制transistor1便携式收音机的时候。他后来告诉我说，他认为这个设计很棒。但我不知道他当时为什么认为我是艾希勒博士的助手，这是后来由汉斯·G.康拉德（Hans G. Conrad）担任的角色，我从来没有担任过这个角色。然而，那时候我已经自认为是我们缓慢壮大的产品设计师群体的发言人了，尽管这一点直到1961年才被正式认定。

relationship with some of the more intractable technicians). The important issue back then – and I feel this is worth mentioning – was to make it clear to the technicians that we did not want to take the work away from them, but to support them. I still had a lot to learn from them, even though I was no layman myself thanks to my own technical and construction education.

Naturally it was also an advantage that the technicians could get hold of me more easily when there was an urgent problem. I could go with them to the drawing board and find a solution better and more quickly than any external designer – and this is a point of view that I hold to this day.

This form of teamwork depends on human consensus. Dr. Eichler always emphasised this too. It only works, however, if you really understand the other person's work, respect their accomplishment and continually re-evaluate their interests. My close relationships with many of the technicians, which in some cases became friendships, developed at that time. I would like to think that, even today, Braun continues to benefit from such personal relationships. Without them you cannot even begin to make acceptable design, and nothing can replace them, no matter how clever your marketing is.

The division of responsibilities in our young department was still not clearly defined. It so happened that Gerd A. Müller took charge of the household appliances, including the shavers, and I took over the flashguns, the new slide projector and the radio sets. Roland Weigend was a sort of "jack of all trades". He made the first models and at the same time drafted the printing templates for the scales.

The new models that we developed in these first years up until 1960 are shown on the following pages.

Most likely Herbert Hirche first got to know my name whilst we were working on the transistor 1 portable radio. He told me later that he thought the design worked well. But why he thought I was Dr Eichler's assistant, I have no idea. This was a role that was later played by Hans G. Conrad – never by me. By then however I already considered myself to be the spokesman for our slowly growing group of product designers – although this did not become official until 1961.

总之，我认为自己绝不是博朗设计的"发明者"，也不是别人想法的执行者。我申请博朗的工作可能是一个意外，但我不认为自己被录取并最终在这里工作了这么久是一个意外。

早期在部门工作的时候，我们关于想法和概念的那种无言的默契，以及那股激昂的创作热情直至今天还让我难以忘怀。

我相信自己之所以能够成为如此重要的"博朗设计"的一部分是因为我一直都是在以"博朗"的方式进行设计，甚至在我听说过这家公司之前就是如此了。

如果现在问我当时是否意识到了自己正在做的事情在10年或20年后会被视为文化史上的开创性工作，我不得不承认那是根本不可能的。

当你积极投入一个事件的整个过程中时，你是无法从外部来看自己的。当然，我也意识到了有一些特别的事情正在发生。我们想让一切变得不同，我们都沉浸于新的变革之中，我们的计划和希望远远超出了我们最终能够实现的范围。虽然称呼我们为"文化先驱"可能有点夸张，但我们取得的成就仍然是值得尊敬的。

就写到这里吧，之后肯定会有一两个具体的问题，我很乐意那时再回答。

致以最良好的祝愿和最热烈的问候！

您真挚的朋友：迪特·拉姆斯

Finally, let me sum up by saying that I in no way regard myself to be the 'inventor' of Braun design. I was also not the executor of the ideas of others. It may have been an accident that I applied for a job at Braun, but I don't think it was an accident that I was taken on and ended up staying for so long.

In the early days there was something that fascinated me, and which I very much miss today: a wordless accord regarding ideas and concepts, and an infectious enthusiasm.

I believe I was able to become such a strong part of it because I had always designed the "Braun" way – even before I had ever heard of the company.

If you ask me today whether I realised back then that I was working on something that 10 or 20 years later would go down as pioneering work in cultural history, I would have to say – no way.

You cannot look at yourself from the outside whilst you are in the middle of an active process. Of course I realised that something special was underway. We wanted to make everything different. We were all caught up in the new spirit of change. We had plans and hopes that reached far beyond what we were capable of ultimately realising. And while it may be a bit grandiose to call us "cultural pioneers", ours was a respectable achievement nonetheless.

That's about all for now. There are sure to be one or two specific questions that I will be happy to try and answer later.

With very best wishes and warmest regards

Your Dieter Rams

注
① 《若阿内斯·波坦特，布拉克尔，50年代的设计》，合著者：奥托·艾舍（Otl Aicher），于尔根·W. 博朗（Jürgen W. Braun），西格弗里德·格罗纳特（Siegfried Gronert），罗伯特·库恩（Robert Kuhn），迪特·拉姆斯和鲁道夫·舍恩温特（Rudolf Schönwandt），科隆，1989年。

Footnotes
1) ... „Johannes Potente, Brakei, Design der 50er Jahre ". With texts by Otl Aicher, Jürgen W. Braun, Siegfried Gronert, Robert Kuhn, Dieter Rams and Rudolph Schönwandt, Köln, 1989.

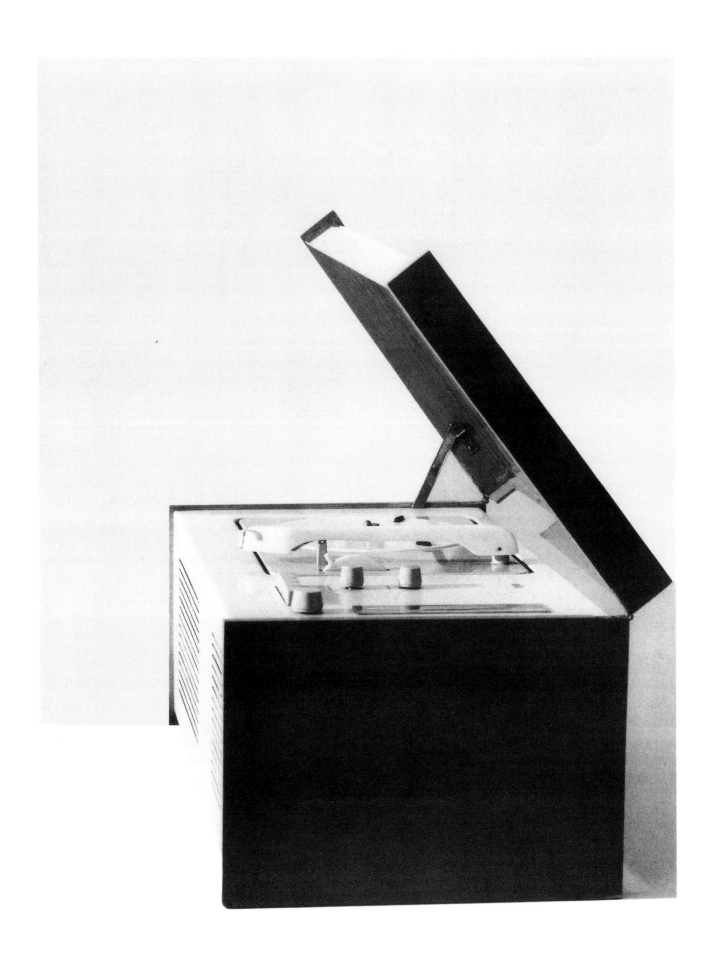

SK 4唱片机与收音机组合一体机（1956年）。所有的操控元件都再次被放置在机身顶部，与20世纪30年代的博朗收音机与唱片机组合一体机的样式相同。机身上的透明盖是一项设计创新，正是由于它的存在，该设备才获得了"白雪公主的棺木"这一绰号

Radio-phono combination SK 4 (1956). The controls were all placed on the top again, as with the Braun radio/phono combination in the 1930s. The transparent lid was an innovation that gave the system the nickname "Snow White's Coffin"

1955年之后的博朗设计

威廉·瓦根菲尔德1954年在达姆施塔特发表的著名演讲中曾说，"唯有实例才令人信服"。他的演讲给欧文·博朗留下了深刻印象，并给博朗的发展带来了决定性的推动力。1955年第一批问世的新款博朗产品确实是令人信服的重要经典实例，因为它们清晰地向我们展示了什么才是"好的设计"。

从那时起，出现了很多关于这些产品设计的文章。然而，令人惊讶的是很少有作者试图理解和描述这种设计方法的核心思想或本质。在我看来，其中最有远见的叙述仍然是理查德·莫斯（Richard Moss）于1962年在美国《工业设计》（*Industrial Design*）杂志上发表的一篇分析文章。

Braun Design after 1955

"You can only convince by example", said Wilhelm Wagenfeld in 1954 in his famous speech in Darmstadt that so impressed Erwin Braun and gave such a decisive impulse to the Braun company. And when the first new Braun products appeared in 1955, they really were convincing examples that were incredibly important and gave form to what we believed to be good design.

A lot has been written about these designs since then. Surprisingly few writers, however, have attempted to understand and describe the core idea, or the essence of this approach to design. One of the most clear-sighted of these still seems to me Richard Moss, who published an analysis in 1962 in the American magazine "Industrial Design".

RT 20桌面收音机（1961年）
Tischsuper RT 20 (1961)

莫斯认为博朗的设计有3条法则：秩序法则、和谐法则和经济法则。这是绝对正确的，而且至今仍然适用。尽管理查德·莫斯在文中只是几笔带过，但文中有关博朗设计的秩序、和谐和经济法则并不是最终目的，也不是构成新"设计风格"的元素，而是出自"设计出功能性的、用户友好型的产品"这个深层次的根本理念，这对我来说才是至关重要的。对于唱片机、厨房用具、幻灯片播放机及剃须刀而言，若是设计成无序的、混乱的、令人困惑或过于浮夸的形式，则无法实现其功能性。同时，设计的和谐及美学品质也有一个功能性的目的：推动产品与用户之间建立积极的情感关系。

According to Moss, Braun is defined by three rules: the rule of order, the rule of harmony and the rule of economy. This is absolutely correct and still applies today. But something Richard Moss only hinted at, and which is of central importance for me, is that the order, the harmony and the economy of Braun design are not self-serving; they are all elements of an entirely new 'design style'. Further, they arise with great consequence from a far deeper intention – to design functional, user-friendly products. A record player, a kitchen appliance, a slide projector or a shaver with disorderly, chaotic, confusing or overloaded design cannot fulfil its functions. The harmony of a design too, its aesthetic quality, also has a functional purpose – it facilitates a positive emotional relationship between a device and its user.

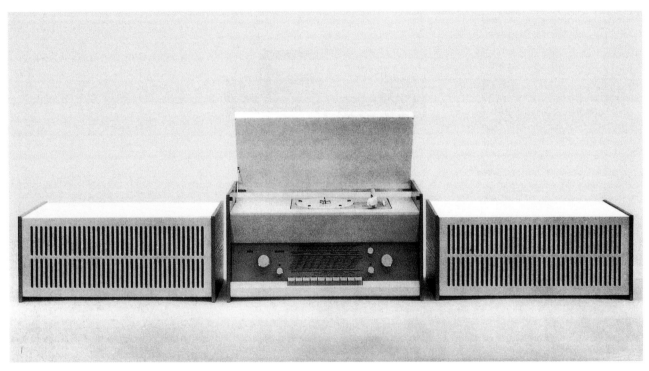

立体声音响控制单元atelier 1及配套的2台L 1外部扬声器，多年来它们一直是博朗产品计划中最重要的设备组合

Control unit atelier 1 with a second, external loudspeaker L 1 – for many years for this was the most important combination within Braun's programme

接续理查德·莫斯总结的3条法则，我想再添加一条影响了博朗设计的第4条法则——持久性。通过专注于必要的功能方面，通过秩序与和谐，通过省略无关的和不必要的东西，我们就可以得到极为简洁的产品设计。它超越了一切浮华时尚，直指本质。

Following from Richard Moss, I would like to add a fourth 'rule' that affects Braun design: longevity. By concentrating on the necessary functional aspects, through order and harmony, by leaving out the incidental and the unnecessary, you arrive at product designs that are extremely concise. They exist beyond all fashion and point towards the essential.

因此，博朗的许多电器可以在总体设计几乎没有变化的情况下连续生产和销售几十年，这一点绝非巧合。

It is therefore no coincidence that numerous Braun appliances could be produced and sold for decades with little change to their overall design.

KM 3厨房料理机（1957年）：这台机器在1993年之前的20多年里一直在生产，外观几乎没有改变过
Kitchen machine KM 3 (1957): This unit was in production, almost unaltered, for well over two decades until 1993

Multimix MX 3多功能搅拌机（1958年）是有史以来最经久耐用的博朗产品之一
The Multimix MX 3 (1958) mixer was in production longen than any other Braun appliance

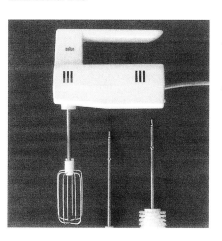

M 1手持搅拌器（1960年）。德国市场上的第一款此类产品，它的推出使得同类产品广受欢迎
Hand mixer M 1 (1960). The first unit of this kind on the German market made this product type popular

Multipress MP 3多功能榨汁机（1957年）
Juicer Multipress MP 3(1957)

SM 3电动剃须刀（1960年）：传说中的带有黑色塑料外壳的sixtant电动剃须刀的前身
Electric shaver SM 3 (1960): The forerunner of the legendary "sixtant" which came with a black plastic housing

PA 1幻灯机（1956年）：德国市场上第一款全自动幻灯机，对于当时成功的博朗闪光灯产品系列来说是一个补充
Slide projector PA 1 (1956): The first fully automatic slide projector on the German market complemented the successful flash programme

T 41便携收音机（1956年）和P 1唱片机（1959年）
Pocket receiver T 41 (1956) and record player P 1 (1959)

在我看来，TP 1收音机与唱片机组合一体机是后来普遍流行的随身听设备的前身
In my opinion, the TP 1 phono combination is an early predecessor of the universally successful Walkman

便携式音响系统

这种以功能为导向的设计一直受到技术发展的强烈影响，并且在未来也将如此。若是当时没有出现新的晶体管技术，我们不可能在20世纪50年代末设计出博朗袖珍收音机。晶体管不仅比真空管小得多，而且所需功率也小得多。晶体管技术的出现意味着我们第一次制造出了可以放在口袋里的收音机。

分别于1958年、1959年和1962年上市的小型晶体管收音机T 3、T 4和T 41是德国最早的一批袖珍收音机。

它们拥有最简单的基本外形——扁平的长方体。产品设计遵循了"少，但更好"的原则。机身外壳由两个热塑性壳拼接而成，这也是我们在此的2年前开发transistor 1便携收音机时的另一个设计创新。T 3产品的扬声器位于方形孔眼罩板的后面，而在其之后1年开发的T 4产品的扬声器罩板的孔眼则是呈圆形排列的。

Portable Sound Systems

Functionally oriented design of this kind has always been strongly influenced by technological development, and will continue to be so in the future. The Braun pocket radios that we designed at the end of the 1950s would not have been possible without the new transistor technology at the time. Transistors were not only far smaller than valves, they also required much less power. This meant that for the first time it was possible to make a radio receiver that you could literally put in your pocket.

The little transistor radios T 3, T 4 and T 41 that came onto the market in 1958/59 and 1962 were amongst the first in Germany.

They had the simplest possible basic form: a flattened cuboid. The design followed the principle of 'less, but better'. The casing was made of two thermoplastic shells, another innovation that we had developed two years earlier for the transistor 1 portable set. The T 3 speaker was situated behind a quadratic perforated area; with the T 4 a year later, the speaker perforations were arranged in a circular pattern.

我们一直特别注重操控元件的设计。每一处设计都经过了深思熟虑，并利用了当时所有的技术。多年来，博朗的设计师们始终在为操控元件的技术改进提出更高效的解决方案。

We always paid particular attention to the design of the operating elements. Every solution was thought through with great care and made use of all technical possibilities. Over the years the Braun designers often suggested highly effective solutions for the technical improvement of operating elements.

T 3/T 31袖珍收音机（1958年）
Pocket receiver T 3/T 31 (1958)

T 4袖珍收音机（1959年）
Pocket receiver T 4 (1959)

T 41袖珍收音机（1962年）
Pocket receiver T 41 (1962)

在T 3及其后续产品的设计中，开/关键和音量控制键被巧妙地嵌入机身外壳。在T 3产品中，用户可以通过一个圆形的拨盘来选择电台。而在后来开发的T 4型号中，整个圆形拨盘被隐藏了起来，只有一个小窗口用来指示所选电台。在同系列产品的第3个型号中，即带有3个波段的T 41中，我们设计了一个几乎是半圆形的窗口，以便更多地显示电台波段。

With the T 3 and its successors, the on/off switch and volume control were sensibly recessed. With the T 3 you could select your station with a circular disc. In later models this disc was hidden and a small window indicated the selected station. With the third model in the series, the T 41, which had three wavelengths, we chose an almost semicircular window display that revealed a larger portion of the scale.

1959年，博朗推出了一款小型唱片机，可以播放当时常见的45转/分的唱片。黑胶唱片可直接放在设备顶部，然后让唱针从下面拨动唱片来播放。这台唱片机的尺寸刚好是参照袖珍收音机的比例设计的，因此这两台设备可以通过一个固定外壳连接并固定在一起，用户可以用手直接提着这台移动的唱片机，这就是后来在全球流行的随身听设备的前身。在那个时代，博朗袖珍收音机和TP 1/TP 2唱片机的组合一体机形式属于绝对的创新。

In 1959 Braun introduced a miniaturised record player for the 45rpm records common at the time. The record was placed on the appliance and played from below. The record player's proportions were exactly oriented around the pocket receiver so both appliances could be fastened together with a handle allowing the user to carry a mobile record player around in his or her hand – it was a forerunner of the international hit called the Walkman. In their time, the Braun pocket radio and the TP 1/2 combination were absolute innovations.

博朗除了生产小型袖珍收音机外，还生产了体型更大、功能更多的transistor 1（1956年）和T 52（1961年）便携式收音机。博朗从20世纪30年代中期开始生产无线便携式收音机，但当时它们的大小和重量都与小型行李箱相当，直到25年后出现晶体管技术，我们才能够生产出真正紧凑的便携式设备。这在当时是一项有趣的设计挑战，即使是在约60年后的今天，我仍然认为其设计是可用的。在transistor 1中，操控元件位于机身顶部的狭窄平面上，调频显示盘位于机身前部，机身上面有一个皮革材质的提带，外壳是由两块塑料壳拼接而成的。随后的T 52型号则是把所有的操作元件都设计在顶部，其中也包括了调频显示盘。这一解决方案在之后的便携式收音机设计中成了固定方案，使得便携式收音机可以用作车载收音机。车主可以将它挂在一个支架上，下车时再取下来。如今，这个设计方案还可以起到防盗作用，但当时这样设计的原因是许多车主根本买不起专门的车载收音机。

Alongside the small pocket receivers there were also the larger, more powerful portable radios transistor 1 (1956) and T 52 (1961). Braun had been producing wireless portable radios since the mid-1930s, but back then they were the size and weight of small suitcases. It took until the advent of transistor technology, a quarter of a century later, for us to be able to produce genuinely compact portables. It was an interesting challenge and with hindsight, some 60 years later, I still find the results acceptable. The operating elements are on a small face at the top and the dial is situated on the front. There is a leather carry strap and device casing comprised of two plastic shells. The subsequent model, the T 52, had all the operating elements situated on top – a solution that became definitive for years in portable radio design. This arrangement also allowed the device to be used as a car radio. For this it was placed in a holder and could be removed when you got out of the car. This solution has become relevant again today for theft prevention, but back then it was because many buyers simply could not afford an additional radio for their cars.

▼ T 521便携式晶体管收音机（1962年）
Portable transistor radio T 521 (1962)

▼ 手柄也可以作为支撑架
The handle is also used as support

▲ 带切向鼓风机的H 1暖风机（1959年）
Blow heater H 1 with tangential fan (1959)

▶ transistor T 2便携式收音机（1960年）：所有操控元件均布置在机身顶部
Portable transistor T2 (1960): All operating elements were arranged on the top

房间与设备

20世纪50年代，受包豪斯（Bauhaus）影响而涌现出的高品质建筑空间与当时博朗新设计的产品之间的关系是不容忽视的，其中特别突出的是音响产品成了定义建筑室内空间的重要元素。在1957年的柏林国际建筑展中，一项名为"interbau"的住房开发项目的样板房几乎都配备了博朗的电器，这一点绝非巧合。当时，弗里茨·艾希勒博士负责博朗的设计和交流，他在1963年写给威廉·瓦格菲尔德的一封信中描述了这种亲和力："新的收音机设备应当很好地配置在良好的现代公寓中，它们应当以令人愉快和自然的方式融入其中。"弗里茨·艾希勒还将弗洛伦斯·诺尔（Florence Knoll）和查尔斯·埃姆斯（Charles Eames）等人设计的现代家具作为博朗设计的参考基准之一。他写道，"我们的产品是为那些希望将室内设计得简单、雅致、实用的人而设计的，它们不是用来实现白日梦的装饰品"。

Rooms and Units

The relationship between the high-quality, mostly Bauhaus-influenced architecture of the 1950s and the new Braun design of the time is unmissable. It is particularly clear with the music systems that became defining interior elements. It was no coincidence that the model apartments at the 1957 international building exhibition 'interbau' in Berlin were furnished, almost without exception, with Braun appliances. Dr Fritz Eichler was responsible for design and communication at Braun at the time and described this affinity in a 1963 letter to Wilhelm Wagenfeld: " The new radio appliances should sit well in good, modern apartments; they should blend in in a pleasant and self-evident manner". Fritz Eichler also cited contemporary furniture such as those from Florence Knoll and Charles Eames as reference points for Braun design "Our systems", he wrote, "were [conceived] for people who want their interiors to be simple, tasteful and practical, not filled with set decoration for unfulfilled daydreams".

Studio 2模块化高保真音响系统（1959年）及配套的LE 1扬声器（1969年），陈列在威斯巴登的诺尔公司展览馆中
Studio 2 (1959) with loudspeaker LE 1 (1969) in the Knoll showroom in Wiesbaden

模块

从20世纪50年代末开始，博朗开发了专门的产品以呈现最纯粹的高质量声音，并为德国的高保真音响发展铺平了道路。我们为首款高保真系统设计的概念是全新的，具有很高的可信度。它们对同类产品领域的设计产生了持久影响，并且延续至今。我们设计了单独的功能模块，如录音机、扩音器、收音机等，它们都可以作为单独的设备使用。这些模块机都具有相同的外观尺寸，这意味着它们可以有机地排列或叠放在一起。

Modules

From the end of the 1950s onwards, Braun developed specialised systems for the purest high-quality sound reproduction and paved the way for high fidelity in Germany. Our design concepts for these first hi-fi systems were completely new and had a high degree of credibility. They influenced design in this product segment in an enduring manner that has not changed to this day. We designed the separate function areas – record player, amplifier, radio, etc. – as individual appliances. These building blocks had the same dimensions, which meant they could be arranged side by side or stacked on top of one another.

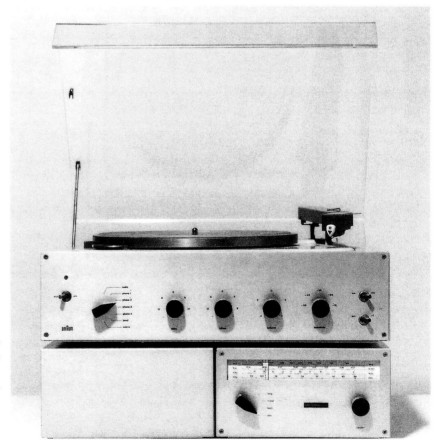

博朗的第一款高保真系统是有史以来最早生产的高保真系统之一。studio 2系统包括CS 11 控制单元、CV 11 扩音器和CE 11 调频器
The first Braun hi-fi system was one of the first hi-fi systems ever produced. The studio 2 system comprised: the CS 11 control unit, the CV 11 amplifier and the CE 11 tuner

LE 1静电扬声器是在获得英国国都公司（Quad）技术许可的条件下生产的，它具有令人印象深刻的音质效果

The electrostatic loudspeaker LE 1 was produced under licence by Quad and had impressive sound quality.

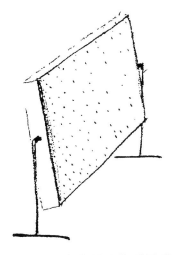

箭头形状的调频开关清楚地指明了其功能和操作方式

The arrow-shaped wavelength switch clearly indicates both function and operation

模块化设计概念的另一个优点是用户可以单独购买模块机，并逐步组合成属于自己的音响系统。因此，高保真系列产品都采用了严谨的长方体形式。机身外壳由带有斜角的钢板制成，正面由拉丝铝材制成。设备的操控元件都是圆柱形的旋钮及带有方向性的开关，其设计和位置布局也都非常严谨细致。我们为每个操控元件专门配置了具有图形化效果、清晰易懂的文字标签，我们还因此专门使用了当时新发明的丝网印刷技术。

我们的创新设计也体现在1960年的博朗 LE 1静电扬声器上。它的机身正面覆盖着一个很大且非常轻的薄金属网格罩板，其发出的音色清晰透彻，令人印象深刻。这款产品非常适合人们当时喜欢听的爵士乐和巴洛克音乐。

Another advantage of this concept was that you could buy the modules individually and put together your own system step by step. The hi-fi units were thus designed in strict cuboid forms. The casings were made of bevelled sheet steel and the fronts from brushed aluminium. The operating elements – which were cylindrical knobs and directional switches – were designed and arranged with great care. We paid particular attention to the product graphics and a clear, easy to understand labelling of the individual operating elements. For this we used a screen-printing technique that was newly invented at the time.

Our innovative design was also visible in the Braun LE 1 electrostatic speakers from 1960. They had a large, very light membrane covering the whole surface, which produced an impressively clear and transparent sound – perfect for the genres of music that we loved listening to at the time: jazz, and also Baroque.

产品系统

Systems

博朗1962年的audio 1设备上的控制单元代表了高保真音响发展的一个里程碑，这其中的原因有很多。首先，晶体管技术的出现使我们在设计时可以完全不考虑电子管，即使是在这样一个大功率的电器中也是如此。因此，我们可以使整个设备的机身高度缩减到只有11厘米。这意味着设备的超薄顶部可以变得既美观又易于操作。其次，audio 1设备的操控元件比SK 4设备更易操作。经常有人评论说，所有这些元件（从调频刻度盘、旋钮、开关到固定螺钉）都是经过精心设计和安排的。正如我们所说，这款设备界面的设计融入了大量的智慧。这样做的目的是制造出一款简单易操作且令人愉快的设备。这款产品与其他更早期的及后来的设备一样都经历了全面而仔细的设计，设计落实到了每一处细节。这一点也通过高品质的音效得到了体现。因此，博朗的高保真音响系统获得了前所未有的赞誉和竞相模仿。

The audio 1 control unit from 1962 represented a milestone in hi-fi development for a number of reasons. Transistor technology made it possible to do without valves completely, even in a powerful electrical appliance such as this. Thus we were able to achieve a height of just 11 centimetres. This meant that the slim top of the module was both easy on the eye and easy to handle. It could also be used better than with the SK 4 for the arrangement of the operating elements. It has often been commented upon that all these elements –from the dials, knobs and switches to the retaining screws – were carefully designed and arranged, and it is true that a lot of brainpower, as we would say today, went into this interface. The aim was to make a unit that was simple, easy and pleasant to operate. As with other earlier, and later, appliances, the thorough, careful design, right down to the details, also intended to reflect the high sound quality as well. As a result the audio hi-fi system reaped praise and imitators like no other.

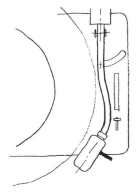

audio 1设备唱臂的手绘设计图
Sketch for the pick-up arm of audio 1

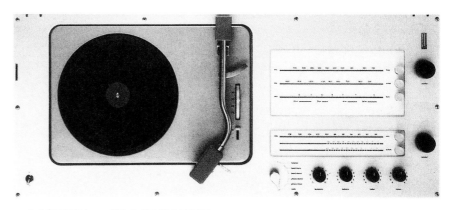

audio 1（1962年）——首次全晶体管化控制器
audio 1 (1962) – the first fully transistorized control unit

我们当时的目标是围绕音频单元开发出一整套音响系统，包括磁带播放机、唱片机及其控制设备、电视和扬声器。这个想法的初衷是让用户可以定制属于自己的音响系统。当然，系统中各个产品的机身比例也进行了相应的调整，各个独立的模块设备可以并排放置或堆叠成一个高塔，甚至还可以安装在墙面上。

Our aim at the time was to develop a sound system around the audio unit – tape player, record player and control unit, as well as a television and speakers. The idea was that you could customise your own system. The proportions were of course harmonised accordingly. The modules could be placed side-by-side or stacked in a tower, they could even be wall-mounted.

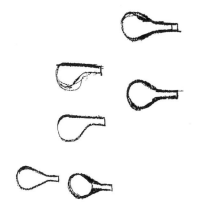

操控开关的手绘设计图
Sketches for the operational switch

对各种模块组件进行组合配置
Reflections on the assembly of various possible components

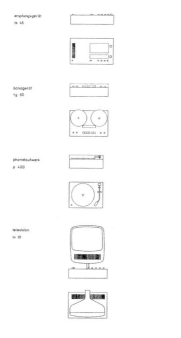

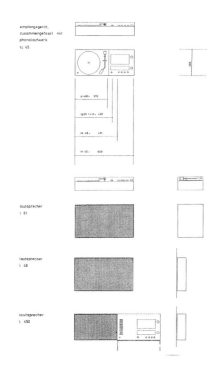

对屏幕可旋转的电视机的设计研究
Design study of a TV set with rotating screen

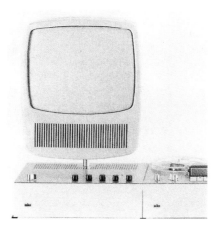

从那以后，我在克伦伯格（Kronberg）家中的办公室就有了这样一个壁挂式音响系统（见第36—37页）。这些设备还可以安装在我设计的维瑟（Vitsoe）606通用货架系统及其他的壁架（Wieser shelf）和框架式搁板系统（String shelf）中。这套音响系统的最初概念来自乌尔姆设计学院的汉斯·古格洛特和赫伯特·林丁格（Herbert Lindinger）。但是，博朗最终并没有生产这个计划中的所有模块单元。博朗于1963年推出第一款磁带录音机TG 60，随后在1965年推出了适合搭配音响系统的FS 600电视机。多年来，audio 1设备之后有许多后续迭代产品（audio 2、audio 250、audio 300），它们在美学设计

I have had such a wall-mounted system in my office in my house in Kronberg ever since (see pages 36 and 37). The units also fitted into the Vitsoe (606) shelving system that I designed, as well as the Wieser and String shelf systems. The initial concepts for this audio system came from Hans Gugelot and Herbert Lindinger at the Ulm School of Design. But, in the end, Braun did not to produce all of the planned modules. The company's first tape player, the TG 60, came onto the market in 1963. This was followed in 1965 by the FS 600 television, which fit the audio system. Over the years there were a number of successor units to the audio 1 (audio 2 / audio 250 / audio 300). They were aesthetically much the same but offered

壁挂式音响模块组件：TS 45调频控制器、TG 60录音机和L 450超薄扬声器
Wall-mounted audio components: control TS 45, tape recorder TG 60 and slim loudspeaker L 450

安装在墙面上的组装系统的手绘设计图
Sketches for a wall assembly

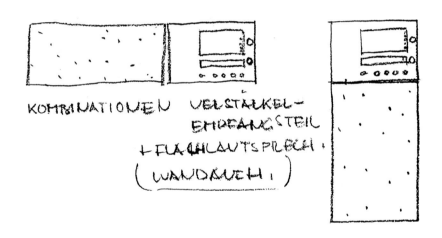

方面几乎是不变的，但是音质方面在经过技术改良后却变得更好了。audio 2还配备了一个新开发的、集成度更好的录音机。

所有音频模块设备都拥有白色或深灰色的钢板外壳及铝制的机身盖板。除了电源开关之外，所有的操控元件都是浅灰色或深灰色的。电源开关和之后的所有高保真音响设备则都是绿色的。在博朗产品中，色彩的使用总是非常谨慎的，并且只用来指示必要的信息。

better sound. The audio 2 came with a newly developed, better integrated record player.

All of the audio modules had sheet steel casings in white or very dark grey. The cover panel was aluminium and the controls were light or dark grey, except the power switch, which, like all Braun hi-fi appliances that followed, was green. Colour was always used extremely sparingly and then only to provide information.

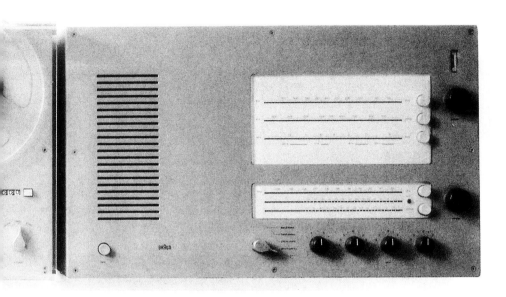

这是一款为放置音响系统而设计制造的特殊桌架，音响系统包含audio 2高保真组合机、TG 60磁带录音机和FS 600电视机
A special base was constructed for the audio system – here with an audio 2, tape recorder TG 60 and the TV set FS 600

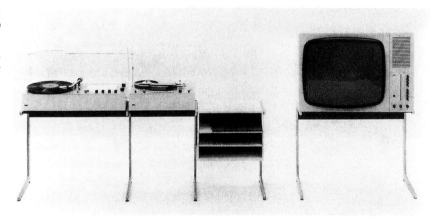

该音频系列产品与之前和之后的所有型号一样，机身背面是光滑整洁的，因此可以立在房间中的任何地方。TS 45调频控制器也像audio 2设备一样将连接件隐藏在控制面板的底部，因此它可以像图示中那样悬挂在墙面上。

As with all previous and subsequent models, the audio series had a smooth, uncluttered back side, so that it could be situated freestanding in a room. With the audio 2 the connections were concealed on the system's underside, allowing the TS 45 control module to be hung on the wall like a picture.

高保真模块单元Studio 1000（1965年）
Hi-fi modular unit studio 1000 (1965)
TG 1000高保真磁带录音机（1970年）
Hi-fi tape recorder TG 1000 (1970)

高保真设备

20世纪60年代初，高保真技术得到了快速发展。1965年，博朗推出一款新的、更大的、模块化的产品系统——studio 1000。它毫无保留地利用了当时的所有新技术，从而拥有了卓越的音质，产品设计也得到了进一步的优化。事实上，studio 1000还开创了黑色高保真音响系统的时代，除了机身正面之外，它的整个机身表面均为浅黑色纹理的漆饰面。

深色的外壳使设备显得更加紧凑，并彰显了它们的高技术特征。studio 1000模块设备还配有带圆形边缘的铝制前面板，这是我们第一次能以足够好的质量所实现的解决方案。这台设备的调谐旋钮尺寸足够大，易于抓握，而设备的开关、旋钮的设计及各种元件的布局则都经过了多次的细致修改。

High Fidelity

In the early 1960s, hi-fi technology continued to develop at a rapid pace. In 1965 Braun introduced a new, larger, modular system called the studio 1000. It took uncompromising advantage of all the technical possibilities available and had excellent sound quality for its time. The design was developed further as well. The studio 1000 heralded the beginning of the era of the black hi-fi system. All surfaces, except the front, were coated in a slightly lightened black structured paint finish.

The dark colour made the units appear more dense and compact and indicated their high technical capabilities. The studio 1000 modules also had aluminium front plates with rounded edges – a solution that we were able to realise for the first time in a good enough quality. The tuning knobs were large and easy to grip and the design of the switches and knobs, as well as placement of various elements, was reworked in even greater detail.

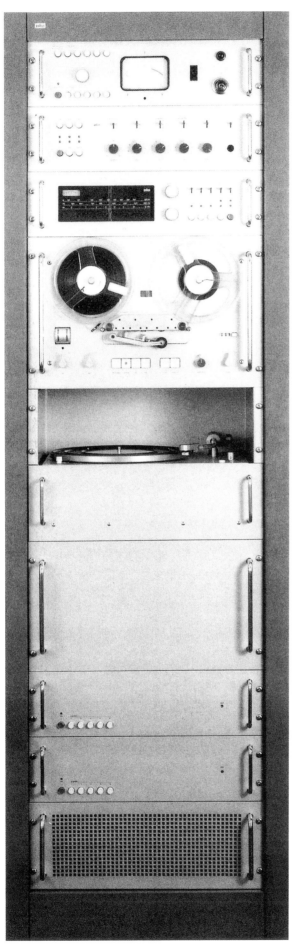

Ela system EGZ专业高保真系统设备（1969年）
Hi-fi Ela system EGZ (1969) for professional use

示波器的设计研究
Design study of an oscillograph

教育游戏设计

对大多数人来说，电子产品及家用电器只是一些"黑盒子"而已，人们完全不知道里面是怎么一回事。博朗作为20世纪60年代领先的电子设备制造商，认为开发出一款教育游戏，并通过一系列简单的实验向孩子们传授电子基础知识是一件既有趣又有意义的事情。

Educational Game Design

For most people electronic and even electrical appliances are just 'black boxes'. You have absolutely no idea anymore about what happens inside. As a leading manufacturer of electronic appliances in the 1960s, Braun felt it would be both interesting and important to develop an educational game that communicated a basic knowledge of

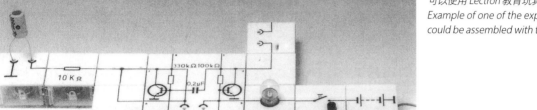

可以使用 Lectron 教育玩具构建的实验电路示例
Example of one of the experimental circuits that could be assembled with the Lectron

于是，我们于1969年推出了以这一理念为指导的Lectron实验和学习系统，它们在创意概念和形式设计上都是全新的。这款产品的诞生是我们与电子工程师、教育工作者和通信专家密切合作的成果。我们的任务是开发出一款教育玩具，它必须简单易懂、功能多样且坚固耐用，以鼓励儿童和青少年以一种创造性和有趣的方式来进行实验探索。

electronics via a series of simple experiments. The resulting Lectron experimenting and learning system, that was introduced in 1969, was brand-new in terms both concept and design. It was designed in close collaboration with electronic engineers, educators and communication experts and our brief was the development of an educational toy that had to be simple, easy to understand, versatile and robust all at once. It was intended to encourage children and teenagers to experiment in a creative and playful way.

专门为机电学习和实验玩具而做的设计，作品名字为"通向按钮的路"（The Way to the Button）（未投入生产）
Design for an electromechanical learning and experimenting toy with the working title: "The Way to the Button" (not produced)

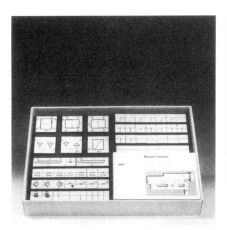

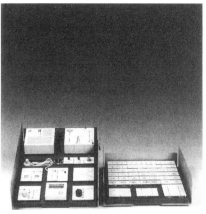

这套Lectron教育玩具包括了一些电子积木块和一本全面的实验指导手册

The Lectron included electronic modules and a comprehensive booklet for experiments

这个系统中含有内置了晶体管、电容器、电阻器或二极管的积木块，学生可以通过将这些积木块连接到金属板上来构建电路。这些积木块是由透明塑料制成的小立方体，白色表面显示了每个积木块的功能，丰富的图形信息说明了电流的方向。

我们曾在1967年设计了一个类似的游戏系统，但最终并没有投入生产。当时的设计主题是电子和机械的结合，目的是让学龄前儿童能够用元件构建出各种简单的机电结构。这个设计方案旨在提供诸如电机和驱动器等功能性的部件，以及齿轮等附加的或连接的部件。所有的积木块都可以相互组装在一起。它与后来开发的Lectron产品一样，主要任务都是创造出简单的玩具，虽然几乎是抽象的，但也是令人兴奋和充满想象力的。

The system had building blocks that contained transistors, capacitors, resistors or diodes that you could use to build circuits by joining them on a metal plate. The building blocks were small cubes made of transparent plastic. Their white surfaces showed the function of each block and illustrated the direction of current with informative graphics.

In 1967, a couple of years earlier, we designed a similar game system that didn't make it into production. The theme here was the combination of electricity and mechanics that would enable pre-school children to build a multitude of electromechanical constructions from a few simple elements. The plan was to provide functional building blocks, such as motors and drives, and additional or connecting elements, such as gear wheels. All the building blocks could be plugged into one another. As with the Lectron, the design's main task was to create a toy that was very simple and easy to understand; almost abstract, yet simultaneously stimulating and exciting to the imagination.

世界波段收音机
The World Receiver

便携式电视机——TV 1000的设计研究（1965年）
Design study for a portable TV set:
TV 1000 (1965)

通过这款世界波段收音机，博朗创造了一个全新的"物种"。它的名字和设计概念都十分新颖，并被一些人认为是博朗10年来最成功的设计之一。它拥有精准的操作界面，即一张散发着魅力的"脸庞"，但其设计从基本外观到最小细节却是始终如一的，从而最佳地实现了其功能性。T 1000世界波段收音机于1963年推出，是一款适用于所有波长的高性能无线电接收机。它通常用于短波接收，但也可以通过附加部件用作导航仪器。一方面，作为便携式仪器，T 1000需要尽可能紧凑和独立的外形；另一方面，作为世界波段收音机，它又需要非常大的体型和众多控制元件。我们的任务则是要使这款产品尽可能明白易懂：用户容易理解它，并且能够自信地操作它。它上面的一个重要元件是位于机身右侧的折叠式波长开关，机身正面的操作面板上还可以覆盖一个保护盖。T 1000世界波段收音机被很多爱好者使用并珍藏，同时它也是博朗开发的最后一款便携式收音机。

With the World Receiver, Braun created a whole new species. The name was as new as the concept for this portable device that was considered by some to be one of the most successful designs of the decade. It had an entirely unmistakable design, a 'face', that radiated fascination, yet it was still consistently designed right down to the tiniest detail to optimally fulfil its function. Introduced in 1963, the T 1000 World Receiver was a high performance radio receiver for all wavelengths. It was often used for short-wave reception but it could also, with additional parts, be used as a navigation instrument. As a portable instrument, the T 1000 needed to be as compact and self-contained as possible, but as a world receiver it needed a very large scale and numerous control elements. Our task was to make the device as self-explanatory as possible. The user should be able to understand it straight away and operate it with confidence. An important element was the foldaway wavelength switch situated on the right side. The operating panel could also be covered with a protective flap. The T 1000 World Receiver, used and treasured for years by aficionados, was to be the last portable that Braun developed.

T 1000世界波段收音机（1963年）——用作收音机和电子通信的便携式设备
World receiver T 1000 (1963): portable units for radio and telecommunication

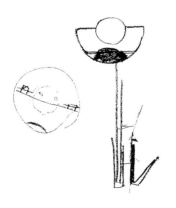

波段开关的初步设计手绘图
Preliminary sketch for the wavelength switch

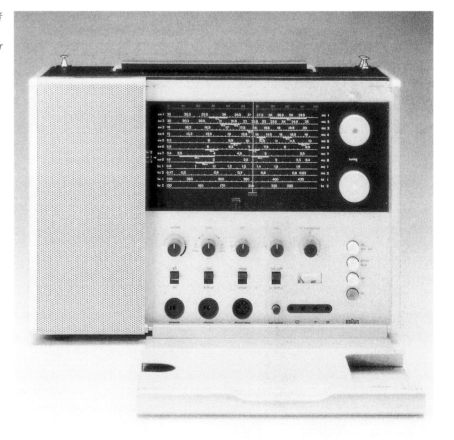

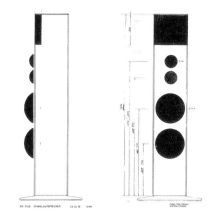

草图: *studiomaster立柱扬声器*
Drawing: studiomaster loudspeaker column

整体演播室系统

博朗的高保真控制设备从 regie 500（1968年）到 regie 550 d（1978年）都有10厘米高，于是我们在开发下一代高性能音响系统时所设定的设计目标是将这一高度减半。因此，我们将所有组件都布置在一块电路板上，这样设备基本上就可以像电路板加外壳罩一样扁平——大约5厘米高。1978年，再找不到其他具有类似容量和性能的高保真音响设备能做到这样紧凑了。整体演播室系统包含RS 1控制单元机、PC 1磁带录音机与唱片机组合一体机。这套系统设备中的单元机可以堆叠起来或并排放置。这些单元机的操控元件都集中在机身狭窄的前面板上。

The integral Studio System

The hi-fi control units from the regie 500 (1968) up to the regie 550 d (1978) were all ten centimetres high. Our aim in the development of the next generation of high performance sound systems was to halve this height. All the components were arranged on a single circuit board so that the unit could be essentially as flat as a circuit board plus casing – which is about five centimetres. In 1978 no other hi-fi unit with comparable capacity and performance was as compact as this. The integral Studio System comprised the RS 1 control unit, and the PC 1 combination record player and cassette deck. The system could be stacked or arranged side by side. The controls were grouped together on the control unit's front panel.

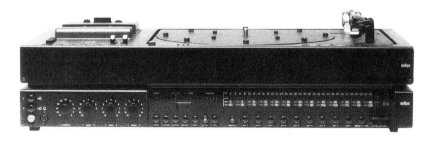

高保真演播室系统（1977年）

Hi-fi integral Studio System (1977)

博朗在20世纪70年代末的另一个重要设计是studiomaster 2150立柱扬声器（1979年），其设计概念也是全新的。它的基本设计理念是为了实现良好的低音效果，将所需的各个大音量组件安装在一个又高又细的立柱中。6个扬声器组件堆叠在一起，低音扬声器和中音扬声器都被一个可拆卸的像圆顶似的罩盖保护起来。这种立柱式扬声器的设计理念至今仍在启发着其他设计同类产品的制造商。

An additional important design of the late 1970s was the studiomaster 2150 speaker tower (1979), whose concept was also totally new. The main reasoning behind the design was to organise the large volume capacity needed for the bass speaker in a tall, narrow column. The six loudspeakers were stacked on top of one another with the low and midtone speakers protected by mesh cages. This idea of a speaker tower continues to inspire the designs of other manufacturers to this day.

studiomaster 2150立柱扬声器（1979年）
studiomaster 2150 loudspeaker column (1979)

20世纪80年代，我们为博朗高保真系统设计了一个模块化的概念，这套系统是博朗的最后一款高保真系统。直到今天，这套设备系统的主要设计和结构仍然是非常令人信服的。根据模块化概念，各个单元机都被设计成具有相同比例的模块。

In 1980, more than 30 years ago, we developed a concept for what turned out to be Braun's last hi-fi system. The principal design and construction of this system has remained convincing until today. The individual units were consequently designed as building blocks with the same proportions.

这些模块单元机机身都被设计为封闭的盒子，并且前面板上都有倾斜的切面
The modules are designed as closed bodies with slanting front panels

左图: atelier模块化高保真系统，配有P 4唱片机、C 4盒式磁带录音机和CD 4光盘播放机（1986年）
Left: Modular hi-fi system atelier, with record player P 4, cassette deck C 4 and CD Player CD 4 (1986)

这些单元机可以堆叠起来或并排放置。这些单元机的机身主体是密封的，机身前端带有一定角度的斜面，这使得它们看起来更纤薄。设备上每个元素的设计都遵循了明确的顺序，而那些很少使用的控制元件则隐藏在机身正面的一个翻盖后面。由于所有输出数据口都被背部的翻盖板遮住了，因此机身背面是完全平整的。此外，机身上还有一个专门设计的设备支撑底座，它可以让这套组合起来的高保真系统直立摆放在房间中。

1990年，也就是在将近60年之后，博朗发布了atelier系统的限量"最新版"，并从此彻底告别了声音再现的世界。

The units can be stacked or laid side by side. The modules' bodies are sealed and angled at the front, which makes them appear even slimmer. Each element's design and positioning follows a clear order and seldom-used elements are hidden behind flaps. The backs of the units are smooth, since all the outputs are also concealed by flaps. A specially designed pedestal allows the atelier system to stand freely in the middle of a room.

In 1990, after nearly six decades, Braun bade farewell to the world of sound reproduction completely with a limited 'Last Edition' of the atelier system.

TV 3电视机的侧视图
The side view of the TV 3

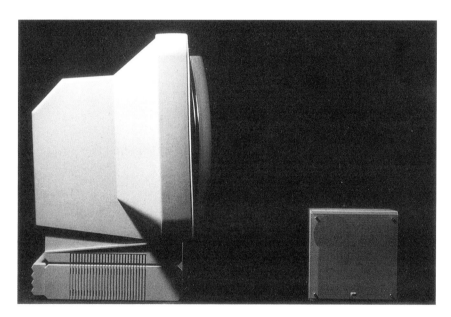

这些模块单元机的机身后面有很大空间，在机身背面有一个活动翻盖，它遮挡住了各种输出连接口，而所有设备的连接线都隐藏在一根软管中
The modules' back sides are generously spaced, outgoing connections covered by flaps, and cables hidden within flexible tubes

带开放式弹仓的D 40幻灯机（1961年）
Slide projector D 40 (1961) with open magazine

D 300幻灯机（1970年）
Slide projector D 300 (1970)

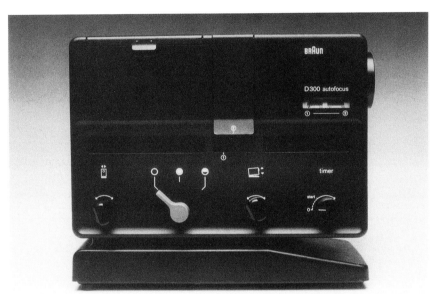

摄影和投影设备

20多年来，我们参与了投影仪、胶卷相机和电子闪光灯的设计。博朗的第一台幻灯机PA 1/PA 2是在1956年生产的，而最后一台博朗摄影设备则是在20世纪80年代初销售的。

回顾过去，我认为这是一个了不起的成就。我们的投影仪、闪光灯和照相机等设备的设计对市场上同类产品的功能和形状的创新产生了巨大的直接影响。以博朗Nizo（Braun Nizo）为品牌在市场上销售的博朗闪光灯、投影仪和超8摄影机无疑是创新的、高性能和高质量的。几十年来，博朗一直是全球同类产品中最重要的制造商之一。

Photography and Projection Units

For more than 20 years we were involved in the design of projectors, film cameras and electronic flash guns. Our first slide projector, the PA 1/2, was produced in 1956 and the last Braun photographic equipment came onto the market in the early 1980s.

In retrospect I think it is a remarkable achievement that our designs for projectors, flashguns and cameras had such a strong direct influence on the creation of functional and shapely product types in this category. The Braun flashguns, projectors and Super 8 cameras, marketed under the name of Braun Nizo, were without doubt innovative, with high performance and quality. For decades Braun was one of the most important manufacturers worldwide of such products.

EF 2电子照相机闪光灯（1958年）
Electronic flash unit EF 2 (1958)

Vario 2000电子照相机闪光灯（1972年）
Electronic flash unit Vario 2000 (1972)

F 900电子照相机闪光灯（1974年）
Electronic flash unit F 900 (1974)

F 1000演播室灯光系统（1966年）——专业级
的强大系统

Studio flash light unit F 1000 (1966) – a high-capacity system for professional use

博朗Nizo摄影机及其各种配件

Braun Nizo cameras with various accessories

Nizo超8摄影机于1965年问世，是为使用当时新的超8电影胶片而生产的。这款产品的设计决定了整个Nizo摄影机系列的样式。尽管后续产品有许多附加的开发和修改，但它的基础外形在近20年的时间里几乎保持不变。这种设计上的连续性有助于延长每一台设备的使用寿命，并让用户能够轻松地操作它们，这一点对我们来说是非常重要的，并且多年来已经变得越来越重要。

Nizo摄影机的特色是拥有阳极氧化铝材质的前面板和侧面板，后来又出现了外壳全部为黑色的版本，如1972年发布的S 1小型超8摄影机。1979年发布的最后一款Nizo摄影机是整合了录音功能的Nizo integral超8摄影机，打破了这种传统的经典金属外壳样式。Nizo integral超8摄影机的外壳几乎完全是塑料材质的。

The Nizo S 8 came out in 1965 and was made to take the new Super 8 film cassettes of the time. Its design defined the form of the Nizo cameras and it remained much the same for almost 20 years, despite many additional developments and modifications. This design continuity, which contributed to the longevity of every single device and allowed the user to familiarise themselves with them easily, was very important to us – and in my view it has become an increasingly important issue ever since then.

The anodised aluminium front and side panels were characteristic for the Nizo cameras.

Later on there were all-black variations, such as the small S 1 from 1972. It was only the last Nizo, the 1979 integral sound camera, that broke with the traditional metal casing and was made almost entirely from plastic.

相比博朗的其他产品，摄影机产品在设计上对重量更轻、更易于处理和操控的需求更大，因为使用不当将会导致拍摄抖动和失焦。因此，我们特别重视处理这方面的问题。我们发现，带有长而平滑的手柄（边缘呈圆弧状，位于平衡重心的下方）的摄影机最容易平稳地操作。同时，我们还可以将电池储存在长手柄中，而握住手柄的食指可以操作位于摄影机底座前部的开关键。在实际拍摄过程中需要用到的功能主要是变焦，而它的调节按钮位于手柄顶部。另外，握持摄影机的手也会产生反作用力，有助于防止设备抖动。此外，大多数人习惯用右手拿着摄影机，所以我们把参数设置和控制功能的按键都放在了左手边。

对于摄影机产品而言，机身上的图形标识必须要清晰明确并指明操作功能，这一点是非常重要的，这款产品的机身上就有一个红点用于表示常规拍摄的标准设置。但是，在后来开发的整合了录音功能的Nizo摄影机中，我们为这个常规设置功能又开发了另一种设计解决方案。我们将各个矩形开关键排列成一行，而各个开关键的中间位置就是之前由红点标记所确定的常规标准设置的位置。

Perhaps more than any other Braun product, a camera needs to be light and easy to handle and operate. Faulty use leads to wobbly and out of focus filming. We thus addressed ourselves with particular intensity to the issue of handling in this case. We discovered that a camera form with a long smooth grip – one that is well rounded at the edges and situated below the centre of balance – is the easiest to operate smoothly and steadily. The batteries can be stored in the handle and the index finger of the holding hand can operate the on-switch situated at the front of the camera base. Functions needed during actual filming, primarily the zoom, are situated on the upper part of the handle. The hand holding the camera also generates counterpressure, which helps prevent camera wobble. We put the settings and control features on the left-hand side since most people tend to hold a camera with their right hand.

Product graphics, as in the clear and explicit labelling of the operating instructions, are also of great importance with a camera. There was, for example, a red dot indicating the standard settings for normal filming, but with the Nizo integral we developed another solution for this task with rectangular switches arranged in a row. Here, the middle

Nizo S 1超8摄影机（1972年）及FP 25电影放映机（1971年）
Super 8 camera Nizo S 1 (1972) and projector FP 25 (1971)

Nizo 6080超8录音摄影机（1980年）
Super 8 sound camera Nizo 6080 (1980)

各个矩形开关键可以向上或向下滑动以进行特殊参数设置。这意味着用户不仅可以一眼看到摄影机上的设置，还可以通过手指切实地体验设置过程。

20世纪70年代中期之前，Nizo生产的都是无声的摄影机。Nizo的第一台有声摄像机是Nizo 2056摄影机，它需要配备更大的胶片盘，同时还需要配备一个额外的录音装置。因此，原来垂直设计的手柄已经不再适合这种更大、更重的摄影机了。所以，我们经过大量的研究后提出了一种新的配置方案。我们将录音组件设置在摄影机的机身下方，手柄改为向前倾斜并远离机身。这个前倾的手柄还可以像专业摄影机的手柄那样折叠并插进一个支撑肩托里面。同时，手柄的前倾设计也使得该设备的录音和操控变得更加便捷。

position was the normal position as defined by the previous red dot mark. The switches could be slid up or down for special settings, which meant that you could not only see the settings on the camera at a glance, but also feel them with your finger.

Nizo produced silent cameras until the mid-1970s. The first sound camera was the Nizo 2056 sound, which required larger cassettes. The camera also needed an additional component for sound recording. A vertical grip would have been unsuitable for this larger, heavier camera, so after much research we came up with a new configuration. The sound component was placed beneath the camera body and the grip was angled forwards, away from the body. This angled handle also had a fold-out shoulder support, similar to those on professional cameras. This allowed the Nizo sound to be operated and controlled very smoothly.

FP 1电影放映机（1964年）
Film projector FP 1 (1964)

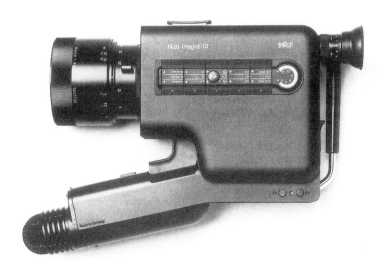

Nizo integral带录音功能的摄影机（1979年）　　　Sound camera Nizo integral (1979)

visacoustic 1000立体声有声电影放映机（1976
年）及其控制单元机（1977年）
Sound film projector visacoustic 1000 stereo
(1976) with control unit (1977)

香烟打火机 / Cigarette Lighters

博朗打火机的设计深受"少，但更好"原则的影响。打火机产品的基本形状为圆柱体、扁平长方体和立方体。我们尝试将它们设计成可供个人使用、把玩的迷你雕塑品，同时，这些迷你雕塑品的样式非常简单，价值完全来源于产品的精致和细节。

The design of the Braun cigarette lighters was strongly influenced by the 'less, but better' principle. The basic forms were cylinders, flattened cuboids and cubes. With them we attempted to design small sculptural objects for personal use that were simultaneously very simple and whose value arose from the precision and attention to detail.

T 2 cylindric 打火机（1968年）
Cylindric lighter T 2 (1968)

F 1 mactron打火机（直线型）（1971年）   *Mactron lighter F 1 / linear (1971)*

我们旨在把它们打造成一种可以被拿着、操作、观赏并被放在口袋里的小乐趣。对我来说，设计打火机一直是一项令人愉快的任务。T 2桌面台式打火机因其形状而被称为"cylindric（圆柱形的）"，它是我为博朗设计的第一款打火机。它有一个很有创新性的磁点火装置，用户按下按钮即可产生提供点燃火花的电荷。由于这样做需要耗费一点力气，所以从气缸壁上切出来的点火按钮的表面被设计得特别大，并且正好位于手握打火机时拇指可以施加最大压力的位置上。

磁点火方式在后来被压电点火方式所取代。在压电点火方式中，电火花也是通过压下按钮产生的，因此不需要使用电池来提供动力。而圆柱形打火机的第3个版本，即1974年发布的energetic型号，则是由位于圆柱体顶部的太阳能电池及点火开关来共同提供能源动力的。cylindric打火

They were meant to be a pleasure to hold, operate, look at and put in your pocket. Designing lighters was always a delightful task for me. The T 2 table lighter, called 'cylindric' because of its shape, was the first lighter that I designed for Braun. It had a magnetic ignition that was quite innovative. The electrical charge to supply the spark was created by pressing the button. Because some force was needed for this, the button surface, that was partially cut out of the cylinder wall, was particularly large and situated exactly where the thumb pad can exert the most pressure when the lighter was held in the hand.

The magnetic ignition was later replaced with a piezo electric ignition. Here again the power for the spark was generated by pressing the button, so no battery was needed. A third version, the 1974 energetic, was powered by solar cells that were situated on the top along with the ignition opening. The cylindric was a

机是一款成功的产品，它连续生产了近20年，直至20世纪80年代中期博朗完全停止生产打火机为止。

在cylindric打火机发布后的几年里，磁点火装置的微型化使得制造袖珍打火机成为可能。博朗在1971年推出的mactron打火机可以通过用拇指将打火机盖子推向一侧来点火，也就是在打开燃烧室的同时触发点火装置。

如果你想帮别人点火，它的盖子还可以一直保持在打开的位置上。mactron打火机后来也推出了压电点火的版本。

1970年开发的domino桌面台式打火机最初使用的是电池供电的点火装置，但由于后来改成了压电点火装置，所以又为打火机重新设计了侧面的按钮。这款打火机被认为是适合年轻人使用的经济型打火机，它的形状像一个立方体，带有柔和的圆角和边缘，顶部有一个明显的凹陷，以用于点火开口。domino桌面台式打火机的外观有不同的三原色版本，并可以与色彩匹配的圆柱形烟灰缸搭配，从而构成一组打火机套装。

successful product and remained in production for almost 20 years until the mid-1980s when Braun ceased producing lighters altogether.

In the years following the introduction of the cylindric, it became possible to miniaturise the magnetic ignition enough to make a pocket lighter. The mactron, introduced in 1971, could be lit by pushing the lid to one side with the thumb, which opened the combustion chamber and at the same time lit the flame.

If you gave someone a light, the lid could be fixed in an open position. The mactron also later came in a piezo ignition version.

The domino from 1970 initially worked with battery-powered ignition, but later with piezo ignition, requiring a redesign of the button on the side. It was conceived as an economical lighter for younger people. It was shaped like a cube with softly rounded corners and edges and a clear dip on the top for the flame opening. The domino came in a variety of primary colours and as a set together with cylindrically shaped, matching ashtrays.

domino 桌面台式打火机（1970年）
domino table lighter (1970)

色彩

Colour

我一直主张在博朗的设计中不使用鲜艳的色彩，产品的主要色彩通常都是白色、浅灰色、黑色或金属色（如天然的或阳极氧化铝和丝绒铬的基本色），只有少数产品是红色、黄色或蓝色的且大多是用于生活区域的电器，如咖啡机、烤面包机、时钟或桌面台式打火机。设计这些有着鲜艳色彩的设备旨在将它们作为替代品，提供给那些想要通过电器而不是花束或其他不符合房间整体和谐的装饰物来为环境增添强烈色彩的人。

这些年来，对于色彩使用的克制来自博朗设计理念的核心原则之一，即个人长期密集使用的电器应该尽可能不引人注目。即它们应该风格低调，与周围的环境融为一体。浓烈的色调可能会令人烦恼

I have always been against the use of bright colours at Braun. The main colours were always white, light grey, black or metallic colours such as natural or anodised aluminium and velour chrome. Very few products were red, yellow or blue. Most of these were appliances for the living area − such as coffee machines, toasters, clocks or table lighters −that were offered as product alternatives for individuals who wished to add strong colour accents to their environments via appliances rather than with bunches of flowers or other decorations that did not fit into the overall harmony of the room.

These years of restraint with colour came from one of the core principles of the Braun design philosophy: appliances designed for intense personal use over a long period of

AromaSelect KF 145 咖啡机（1994年）
AromaSelect KF 145 coffee maker (1994)

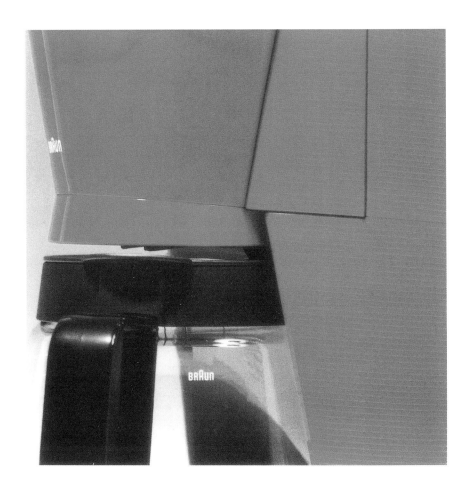

regie 308˚ 接收机的控制元件（1973年）
Control unit regie 308˚ (1973)

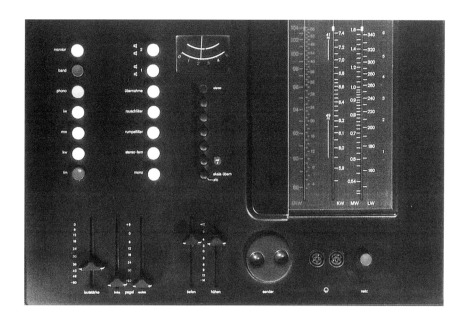

regie 308˚ 接收机的控制元件（细节）
Control unit regie 308˚ (detail)

或激动，而中性色彩的产品可以允许用户根据自己的色彩偏好来设计环境，而且将来也可以更轻松地改变空间环境的色彩。

因此，我们仅在特殊情况下使用鲜艳的颜色进行装饰。另一方面，无论是在过去还是现在，博朗产品上所使用的色彩经常用于指示信息，如应用在高保真音响系统及袖珍计算器中的色彩方案。为此，我们开发了一套已经使用了几十年的色彩编码系统。

time should be as inconspicuous as possible. They should retreat into the background and blend in well with their environment. Strong colour accents can be bothersome or irritating. Colour-neutral products allow users to design their environments according to their own colour preferences – and later change them more easily if they wish.

Therefore we only used colour for decoration in exceptional circumstances. On the other hand colour was, and is, often used for information purposes – in hi-fi systems or pocket calculators, for example. Here we developed a colour coding system that has been in use for decades.

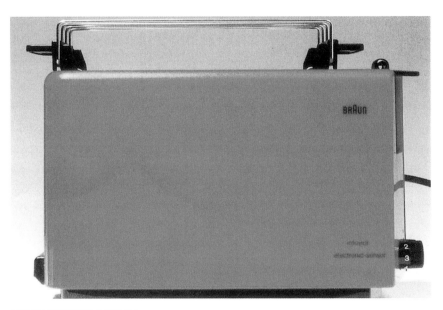

HT 95长槽烤面包机（1991年）
Long-slit toaster HT 95 (1991)

domino T 3 打火机 (1973年)
domino T 3 lighter (1973)

T520便携式收音机（1962年）
Portable transistor radio T 520 (1962)

phase 1 闹钟（1971年）
phase 1 alarm clock (1971)

cassett电池驱动剃须刀（1970年）
cassett battery-operated shaver (1970)

HLD 4 吹风机（1970年）
HLD 4 hairdryer (1970)

domino桌面台式打火机和烟灰缸组合套装（1976年）
domino table lighter and ashtray set (1976)

迪特·拉姆斯和他的团队

设计评论家鲁道夫·舍恩温特（Rudolf Schönwandt）曾就博朗的设计团队及其工作、产品发表评论。本文的部分内容最早在1980年柏林的"设计：迪特·拉姆斯&"（Design: Dieter Rams&）[①]主题展览上发表。

20世纪80年代初，在柏林IDZ[②]举办了一场主题为"设计：迪特·拉姆斯&"的大型展览，展出迪特·拉姆斯的作品。展览名称中的字符"&"指代所有与他共事的人，不仅包括他在博朗所领导的设计部门的设计师、模型师和助手，还包括公司管理者、技术人员和营销人员，他们也为产品设计提供了各方面支持，表现出极大的主动性和鼓励性，并在产品的设计过程中提出了相应的建议或意见。

工业设计尽管几乎总是团队合作，但是，如果有一个人是整个设计过程的指导者，并且设计主要由他来决定，那么我们仍然可以选定他作为产品的设计师。

1993年的团队[③]

迪特·拉姆斯在博朗的核心设计团队由6位工业设计师组成：彼得·哈特温（Peter Hartwein）、路德维希·利特曼（Ludwig Littmann）、迪特里希·卢布斯（Dietrich Lubs）、罗伯特·奥伯海姆（Robert Oberheim）、设计副总监彼得·施耐德（Peter Schneider）和罗兰·乌尔曼（Roland Ullmann）。

此外，还有秘书兼助理罗丝-安妮·伊塞贝特（Rose-Anne Isebaert）、产品平面设计师沃尔特劳德·穆勒（Waltraud Müller）、CAD设计助理加比·登菲尔德（Gaby Denfeld），以及初级设计助理比约恩·克林（Björn Kling）和科妮莉亚·塞弗特（Cornelia Seifert）。克劳斯·齐默尔曼（Klaus Zimmermann）领导了7位建模师：乌多·巴迪（Udo Bady）、赫尔穆特·哈克尔（Helmut Hakel）、罗伯特·肯珀（Robert Kemper）、克里斯托夫·马里亚内克（Christoph Marianek）、奥利弗·米克尔（Oliver Michl）、罗兰·魏根德（Roland Weigend）和卡尔-海因茨·伍特奇（Karl-Heinz Wuttge）。于尔根·格雷贝尔（Jürgen Greubel）之前是团队的固定成员，后来转为自由雇员，他的存在使团队更加完善。[④]

Dieter Rams and his team

The design team at Braun, their work and their products described by the design critic Rudolf Schönwandt. Parts of this text were first published in "Design: Dieter Rams&", Berlin 1980[1)].

In the early 1980s a large exhibition was devoted to the works of Dieter Rams at the IDZ[2)] in Berlin entitled "Design: Dieter Rams&". The '&' at the end referred to all his coworkers −not just the designers in the design department of Braun AG, of which he was head, the model makers and the assistants, but also the employers, the technicians and the marketing people who prepared the way, showed great initiative, encouraged and set goals and with advice or criticism were involved in the products' design.

Industrial design is almost always about teamwork. Nevertheless, singling out an individual as the designer of a product can be justified when he is the one that has steered the design process and when the design has been significantly determined by his hand.

The Team in 1993[3)]

The core of Dieter Rams' design team at Braun consisted of six industrial designers: Peter Hartwein, Ludwig Littmann, Dietrich Lubs, Robert Oberheim, Peter Schneider, the deputy head of design, and Roland Ullmann.

In addition there were the secretary and assistant Rose-Anne Isebaert, product graphic designer Waltraud Müller, Gaby Denfeld the CAD design assistant and the junior design assistants Björn Kling and Cornelia Seifert. There were seven modelmakers led by Klaus Zimmermann: Udo Bady, Helmut Hakel, Robert Kemper, Christoph Marianek, Oliver Michl, Roland Weigend and Karl-Heinz Wuttge. As long-term team member, and later a freelancer, Jürgen Greubel rounded out the team.[4)]

迪特·拉姆斯在与弗里茨·艾希勒博士探讨   *Dieter Rams in conversation with Dr Fritz Eichler*

迪特·拉姆斯曾经在汉堡美术学院[5]任教多年。为了弥补他亏欠学生们的校内教导时间，他为学生们提供了可以在博朗的设计部门工作长达5个月的机会。

本书的编写工作开始于1993年，当时迪特·拉姆斯还是博朗设计部门的负责人。他如今已经63岁了，已将设计部门的职责移交给了继任者彼得·施耐德[6]。1995年5月，博朗的管理委员会授予拉姆斯一个新职位，以表彰他的成就。他现在担任的职务是博朗企业形象事务的执行总监，该职位直接向董事长阿奇博尔德·列维斯（Archibald Levis）汇报工作。

1995年以后的团队

多年来，博朗设计团队的成员几乎保持不变。设计团队始于1956年，当时迪特·拉姆斯接到了来博朗后的第一批产品设计任务。紧随其后，格德 A. 穆勒及建模师罗兰·魏根德、罗伯特·肯珀

Dieter Rams has been teaching for years at the University of Fine Arts in Hamburg[5]. In compensation for his limited presence at the university, he offers his students the opportunity to work for up to five months in the Braun design department.

This book "Less, but Better" was begun in 1993 when Dieter Rams was still head of the design department at Braun. He is now 63 years old and has passed on responsibility for the design department to his successor Peter Schneider[6]. In May 1995 Rams was given a new position by the board of management in recognition of his achievement. He is now Executive Director of Corporate Identity Affairs and in this role is answerable directly to the chairman Archibald Levis.

The Design Team after 1995

The constellation of the design team has remained more or less unchanged for many years. It began in 1956 with Dieter Rams' first product design commissions and the arrival of Gerd A. Müller and the modelmakers Roland Weigend and Robert Kemper at Braun. This

1993年的博朗设计团队

　　以下是博朗设计部门的员工在20世纪80年代中期拍摄的工作照。

The Braun Design Team 1993

The following photos of the Braun design department were taken in the mid-1980s.

彼得·哈特温，工业设计师
Peter Hartwein, industrial designer

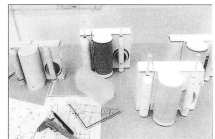

罗丝-安妮·伊塞贝特，秘书兼助理
Rose-Anne Isebaert, secretary and assistant

罗伯特·肯珀，建模师
Robert Kemper, model technician

路德维希·利特曼，工业设计师
Ludwig Littmann, industrial designer

迪特里希·卢布斯，工业设计师
Dietrich Lubs, industrial designer

沃尔特劳德·穆勒，产品平面设计师
Waltraud Müller, product graphics
assistant

罗伯特·奥伯海姆，工业设计师
Robert Oberheim, industrial designer

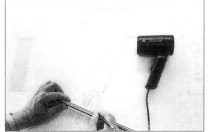

彼得·施耐德，工业设计师、设计副
总监
Peter Schneider, deputy chief of the
design department

罗兰·乌尔曼，工业设计师
Roland Ullmann, industrial designer

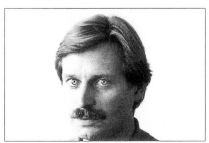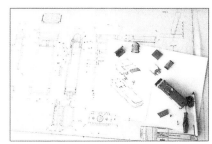

罗兰·魏根德，建模师
Roland Weigend,model technician

克劳斯·齐默尔曼，首席建模师
其他建模师还有乌多·巴迪、赫尔穆
特·哈克尔、克里斯托夫·马里亚内
克、卡尔-海因茨·伍特奇等
Klaus Zimmermann, chief model
technician
Udo Bady,Helmut Hakel, Christoph
Marianek,Karl-Heinz Wuttge

也相继来到了博朗。这种长期合作关系对设计部门的工作氛围产生了特殊影响，博朗的设计部门位于法兰克福附近克伦伯格公司总部的"家"中。

团队成员所承担的职责很多，因此设计团队的规模并不是特别大。要知道，这个部门承担了博朗所有产品的设计。此时的情况已经与早些年的情况不同了，那时还需要乌尔姆设计学院的汉斯·古格洛特、威廉·瓦根菲尔德和赫伯特·赫什为博朗工作，而现在已经不再需要外部设计师的参与了。博朗团队现在开始越来越多地为吉列集团的客户提供服务，如欧乐B（Oral-B）公司和嘉芙瑞（Jafra）公司。

long-term collaboration has had a special impact on the working atmosphere of the design department, which is at 'home' in the company headquarters in Kronberg, near Frankfurt.

Considering their multitude of responsibilities, the design team is not particularly large. It is in charge of the design of all Braun products. Unlike in the early years, when Hans Gugelot from the Ulm School of Design, Wilhelm Wagenfeld and Herbert Hirche worked for Braun, the services of external designers are now no longer required. On the contrary, the Braun team is increasingly involved in commissions for clients within the Gillette group such as Oral-B and Jafra.

近40年间，博朗设计部门共开发了500多种产品，从1956年的T 1便携式收音机到1994年的MultiMix 3手持搅拌器，这还不包括在这期间无数次的重新开发和修改。

作为博朗的总设计师，拉姆斯的职责是指导整个设计部门的工作。他要参与各个项目，了解项目的开发状态，为设计师提供建议，检查产品原型，并在公司内部担负设计部门发言人的职责。然而，他的团队成员都享有很大的独立性。团队成员所负责的产品设计可以算作他们自己的成就，而他们本人也会因此收获来自公司内部和外部的赞誉。

Over the course of four decades, the Braun design department has developed more than 500 individual products – from the T 1 portable radio from 1956 to the 1994 MultiMix trio hand mixer – not to mention innumerable redevelopments and modifications.

The chief designer steers the work of the department. He is involved in the individual projects, knows their state of development, advises the designers, checks the prototypes and represents them to the company. At the same time his team enjoys a great deal of independence. The designs of the products that they are responsible for are their own accomplishments and they are credited both internally and externally for them.

注
①这部分内容在第一版中是于1995年完成的。同年，迪特·拉姆斯被任命为博朗公司企业形象事务的执行总监。从那以后，他原来团队的许多员工都离开了公司。1995年，彼得·施耐德接管了设计部门，拉姆斯则于1997年彻底离开公司。自2009年以来，奥利弗·格拉布斯（Oliver Grabes）负责领导博朗设计部门。
②柏林国际设计中心
③同①。
④在拉姆斯领导设计部门期间，博朗设计团队的其他成员还包括赖因霍尔德·韦斯（Reinhold Weiss）、理查德·菲舍尔（Richard Fischer）、罗兰·乌尔曼和弗洛里安·塞弗特（Florian Seiffert）。
⑤1981—1997年，拉姆斯担任设计系教授。
⑥同①。

Footnotes

1) Ed. note. This chapter was completed for the first edition of this book in 1995. In the same year, Dieter Rams was appointed director of Corporate Identity Affairs at Braun. Many of the employees from his original team have since left the company. In 1995 Peter Schneider took over Dieter Rams's design department; Rams left the company completely in 1997. Since 2009 Oliver Grabes has led the Braun design divison.

2) Internationales Design Zentrum Berlin

3) Ibid. 1

4)Ed. note: Additional employees of the Braun design team during Rams's time that should not go unmentioned are: Reinhold Weiss. Richard Fischer, Roland Ullmann and Florian Seiffert.

5)He was professor of design from 1981 to 1997.

6)Ibid. 1

竞争

多年来，博朗的每位资深设计师都专注于某一特定的产品领域，如剃须刀、家用电器、钟表、头发护理产品等。这种专业化分工是有意义的，因为对于工业设计而言，特别是对于博朗所理解的设计，如果设计师没有深厚的专业技术知识和对相关产品类别的全面了解，他们将无法完成设计。博朗的设计师在许多领域都需要高水平的专业知识，他们还需要与营销部门和技术部门的合作伙伴进行密切的个人交流。在开发新产品的过程中，设计师需要与这些合作伙伴进行长期而深入的合作。但是，公司内部的专业化分工机制并没有使各个设计师之间的专业交流变得困难。有时候，个别项目还会移交给不同的设计师，但责任始终是由相关的高级设计师来承担的。

Competence

Over the years, each senior designer has come to specialise in a particular product area, be it shavers, household appliances, clocks, hair care or whatever. This specialisation makes sense since industrial design –and particularly design as Braun understands it–is not possible without profound technical know-how and thorough familiarity with the relevant product category. The designers need a lot of knowledge about many different areas. They also need close, personal contact with their partners in the marketing and technical departments with whom they need to work long and intensively during the development of a new product. This specialisation is not so pronounced as to make the constant professional communication between the individual designers difficult. Occasionally individual projects are handed over to different designers, although responsibility always remains with the relevant senior designer.

组织

设计部门应该如何融入、在哪里融入公司组织？这个问题在外人看来似乎是次要的，但它实际上是设计师开展工作时最重要的先决条件之一。

Organisation

How and where is the design department integrated into the company's organisation? This may seem a secondary aspect to the outsider, but it is in fact one of the most important prerequisites for the work of a designer.

责任

　　博朗设计师的主要职责是对产品进行全面设计，包括整体设计和所有的细节设计。他们确定了产品的基本形式、尺寸比例、操作元件的排列布局、外观结构和色彩的设计及产品标识（产品上的所有文字和符号）。产品附带的所有东西，包括容器、磁带、附件、清洁工具等，也都是由设计部门设计的。设计师同样还要积极参与材料的选择，从生态环保的角度来说，这一点在如今已经变得越来越重要了。

Responsibilities

The main task of the Braun designers is the comprehensive design of a product – as a whole and in all of its details. They define its basic form, the dimensions and the proportions, the arrangement of the operating elements, the design of the surface structure and colour as well as the product graphics – all the writing and symbols on the product. Everything that belongs to a product, including the containers, cassettes, accessories, cleaning implements, etc., is also designed in the design department. The designers are equally closely involved in the selection of materials, an aspect that today, in ecological terms, is of increasing importance.

设计师在产品开发过程中的作用

为了能够全方位参与产品的设计，博朗的设计师们从一开始就积极参与每一款新产品的开发。他们围绕产品的基本概念密切合作，并以"设计工程师"的身份与技术部门深入合作，以找到提高产品的实用性、创造性和建设性的解决方案。多年来，设计师们为博朗的产品创新提供了巨大动力。他们对技术创新、新型材料和制造方法都了然于心。

The Designers' Role in the Process of Product Development

In order to design so comprehensively, the Braun designers have to be significantly involved in the development of every single new product. They collaborate closely on the initial concept of the product and function as design engineers with the technical department to discover new design-construction solutions that improve product utility. Many innovative impulses have come from the designers over the years. They are conversant with technological innovations and familiarise themselves with new materials and innovative methods of production.

有个例子既可以很好地说明设计工作以技术为导向，又可以体现出设计师在产品开发过程中的参与程度有多大，那就是兼具了硬质与软质表面的外壳设计。关于博朗的手持设备，如剃须刀，其设计重点是让用户更容易、安全地握持，因此它们需要拥有一个具有良好抓握力的防滑外壳。1977年，博朗micron电动剃须刀上市，它的表面结构在当时就是创新的设计，带有很多按钮状的小凸起。这种带凸起的肌理结构既容易抓握，也容易保持清洁。不过，设计师想要做的是更进一步果断地改良外壳表面，使剃须刀具有更高的实用价值。因此，设计师选用了比外壳其他部分更柔软的材料来制造小凸起。这种软凸起结构使剃须刀握起来

An example of this technically-oriented design work that shows how deeply involved these designers are in the process of product development is the design of casings with hard and soft surfaces. Hand-held devices, such as shavers, should be easy and safe to hold. They need a surface with good grip. The Braun micron electric shaver that came onto the market in 1977 had a surface structure that was completely new at the time, with small button-like, convex 'dots'. This knobbly structure was absolutely easy to grip and was also easier to keep clean. The designers' intention, however, was to decisively improve the surface structure and thus give the shaver an even higher utility value. They came up with 'dots' made from a material that is softer than the rest of the

更舒适，触摸起来也更舒服。此外，凸起还可以有效防止剃须刀从水池边缘等潮湿或倾斜的平面上滑落。

但是，怎样实现这个硬质外壳加上软质凸起的设计理念呢？对于外行人来说，这项任务所要求的技术条件有多么复杂是很难想象的，而且这些条件有时是设计师也无法逾越的难题。他们必须找到合适的材料、合适的结构，以及合适的生产方法。当时，这项创新最早是由设计师们发起的，也是由他们不断推进的，旨在制造出有最佳触感的外壳表面结构。

casing. This soft dot structure would make the shaver more comfortable to hold and more pleasant to the touch. They would also prevent the shaver from slipping off wet or angled surfaces such as the edge of the sink.

But how to realise this idea of a hard shell with a soft dot structure? It is hard for the layman to imagine the complex technical requirements this task demanded and that seemed at times insuperable to the designers. They had to find the right materials, the right construction and, most importantly, the right method of production. This new invention was initiated by the designers, kept going by them and directed towards their aim of a tactually optimal surface structure.

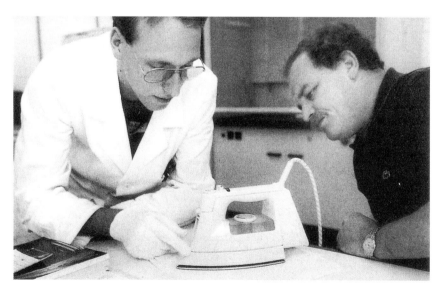

最终，在材料技术人员、设计师、生产技术人员，以及塑料制造厂的应用技术人员的长期通力合作下，这种新型的（当然也是获得了专利的）硬外壳兼软凸起的表面结构被制造了出来。

The new (and of course patented) hard-soft surface was finally realised thanks to a long and intensive collaboration between material technicians, construction and manufacturing engineers as well as the extremely competent applications engineers at the plastics manufacturers.

同样，通过这种多方合作的方式，我们也取得了从产品的基本结构到操作元件的设计等技术成就。这些成就只有在设计师和技术人员相互尊重并通力合作的基础上才能获得。

方法

在生活的许多领域中，取得成功的关键是拥有正确的方法。在某种程度上说，设计也是如此。作为"设计工程师"的设计师，他们在新产品开发的复杂协作过程中不仅要完成自己的特定工作，还必须适应结构化和有序的公司内部规范，如产品的设计方案需要在某个特定的截止日期前以某种特定的方式提交等。

如果设计任务是要求采用"找形"（form finding）这个特定领域的方式，那么设计师也会照此提出一套精心构思的方法。可以说，他们的方法总是根据具体的问题而灵活变化的。

Many other design solutions were reached in a similar way – from the basic structure of a product to designing the operating elements – technological achievements that were reached only through mutually respectful collaboration between designers and technicians.

Methods

The right methodology is the key to success in many areas of life. This is also true for design – within limits. As much as the designers, in their role as 'design engineers', fulfil their particular job in the complex collaborative process of new product development, they must also fit into the structured and ordered company framework. This means, for instance, that the design of a product needs to be defined in a particular way by a particular deadline.

The designers also follow a well-planned – methodical if you like – path in the specific field of 'form finding'. Their methodology here follows the logic of the matter at hand.

博朗的设计师在开始每一个新项目时都会千方百计地彻底了解与该设计相关的一切信息，包括技术方面、当前的市场情况的信息，尤其是要深入了解产品目标用户的需求和愿望。无论是手持搅拌机、钟表、厨房用具，还是吹风机，如果不了解并充分理解用户的众多需求，那么就无法设计出具有实用功能的工具。

Braun designers start each new project by thoroughly informing themselves about everything that could be relevant to the design in any way whatsoever – the technical aspects, the current market, and most particularly the needs and wishes of the people who will use the product. From hand mixers, clocks and kitchen appliances to hairdryers, no tool

因此，设计师们会反复思索，并试图找到一个设计概念作为设计的起点。这个设计概念应对已有的想法提出令人信服的进一步发展。设计师要先明确自己的目标，然后再与技术人员和营销人员进行交流以了解他们的目标。这些人会先评估设计师的想法的成功率，然后再共同计划下一步工作。工业设计首先是头脑的抽象化工作，但这些想法将通过讨论和验证一步步变得具体化。在下一阶段，设计师会继续以这种方式进行工作。他们会把最初的设计理念用图纸或由简易材料制成的初级模型展示。迪特·拉姆斯称这些模型为"三维草图"。现在，设计师展示最终设计方案的主要工具已经变成了计算机，而且产品的形式也不再需要通过图纸或模型等模拟的方式来确定，而是以数字的方式来确定。CAD软件将设计师与技术人员直接联系起来，这些技术人员包括研发专家、结构工程师、质量工程师及生产计划员，他们通常都与新项目的设计开发并行工作。如今，即使是最终的原型产品也是由计算机控制的机器制造的。

通常，设计概念越具体，产品模型就越精确、逼真，仅凭肉眼很难将它们与同款的真实产品区分开来。

同时，为产品批量生产的准备工作提供支持也成为设计师的一个重要职责。正是因为如此，设计师必须从一开始就牢记要找到有助于高效生产的设计解决方案。如今，博朗有着高效、高度自动化、高科技的生产工序，而在这样的基础上进一步提高生产效率已经变成了一项非常具有挑战性的任务。同时，设计师的工作如今还包括确保在设计阶段使产品原型达到预期的质量水平，以及在批量生产阶段也要能够保持这种质量水平。

of this kind can be functionally designed without knowing and fully understanding the many and complex requirements of the user.

The designers reflect on the task at hand and try to find starting points for a design concept that promises a convincing further development of existing ideas. They define their goals, and talk to the technicians and marketing department to find out their aims as well. They evaluate the chances of success for their ideas and plan the next steps together. Industrial design is first and foremost a job for the mind. But these thoughts will be made concrete step by step, by putting them up for discussion and verifying them. In the next phase the designers work in an analogue way – the first design ideas will be embodied in drawings or early models made of materials that are easy to work. Dieter Rams calls these "threedimensional sketches" . Today the main tool for the final definition of the design is the computer. The form of a product is no longer defined in an analogue fashion – through drawings or models – but digitally. CAD, Computer Aided Design, links the designers directly to the technicians – the research and development experts, the construction and quality engineers and the production planers, who all work parallel to the development of a new project to a large extent. Even the final prototypes are made with computer-controlled machines these days.

The more concrete the design concept, the more precise and better the models turn out. They can be hard to distinguish from the serial product with the naked eye.

Support for the manufacturing engineering in preparation for serial production has also become an important field of responsibility for designers. This is why they must always bear in mind right from the beginning that they need to find design solutions that facilitate efficient production. With today's highly efficient, highly automated, high-tech production processes at Braun, this has become a challenging task. At the same time it is also the designer's job to ensure that the levels of quality intended at the design stage really are reached and then maintained when it comes to series production.

KF 20咖啡机（1972年）   Coffee maker KF 20 (1972)

咖啡机，意式浓缩咖啡机

20世纪70年代初，我们设计了博朗的第一台咖啡机。相比其他电器，咖啡机的功能和结构允许我们在更宽泛的范围内进行基本设计。设计这款产品时，我们也是从一开始就参与了产品的开发过程。KF 20咖啡机的外观形式就是根据咖啡的制作流程设计的。机器顶部是加热水的水箱，水箱正下方是过滤咖啡粉的滤芯元件，底部是放在加热盘上的水壶。这种符合操作逻辑的结构设计最终形成了一个细高的封闭式圆柱形产品，这个设计形式在当时是全新的。机身上的两根金属管将加热盘连接到了设备顶部。这款咖啡机还有几种不同颜色的版本供客户挑选。

Coffee Makers, Espresso Machines

In the early 1970s we worked on our first coffee makers. Function and construction permit more scope for an expedient basic design with these than with other electric appliances. Here, too, we were involved in the development process right from the beginning. The form of the KF 20, for example, followed the process of coffee preparation. At the top was the tank where the water is heated, directly below it the filter element with the coffee grounds and then the pot sitting on the hotplate. This logical configuration led to a slim, self-contained column shape that was completely new at the time. Two metal pipes connected the hotplate to the top of the appliance. The machine was produced in several different colour variations.

KF 40咖啡机（1984年）：从顶部俯视可以看到一种创新的结构——两个相交的圆柱体
Coffee maker KF 40 (1984): The top view shows an innovative construction: two intersecting cylinders

Aromaster KF 40咖啡机带有凹槽的水箱外壳，电线的存储空间位于机身背面
Grooved water tank housing of the Aromaster KF 40 with a cable storage space at the back

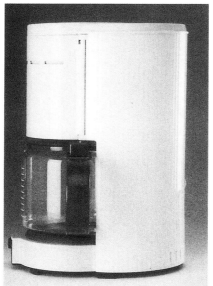

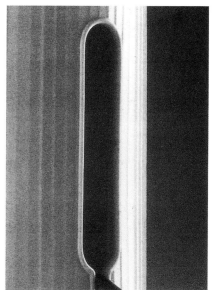

咖啡机的样式紧凑简单，非常适合家居环境。不过，它虽然很受欢迎，尤其是被设计爱好者所青睐，但是它还有一个需要改进的地方：该设备需要2个加热元件，一个在顶部加热水，另一个在底部加热咖啡。

　　对于后续的系列型号Aromaster KF 40（1984年），技术人员和设计师共同为其研发了一种升级装置，该装置保留了原机封闭式的细长柱身，但整机只需要一个加热元件。他们通过在装有滤芯和玻璃咖啡壶的主圆筒机身背面包裹上一个半圆形的水箱解决了加热元件问题。

It was compact, simple and fitted well into a living environment. Nevertheless, despite its strong popularity – particularly amongst design fans – it had a weakness that necessitated further development: the appliance needed two heating elements, one at the top to heat the water, and another at the bottom to keep the coffee warm.

For the follow-up model, the Aromaster KF 40 (1984), the technicians and the designers found a configuration that retained the self-contained, slim column, yet required only one heating element. They did this by wrapping a semi-cylinder for the water tank around the back of the main cylinder that contained the filter element and the coffee pot.

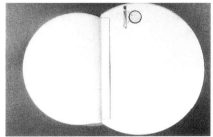
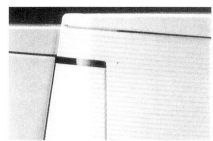

Aromaster KF 40的外壳由塑料制成，价格更低廉，但是制造技术要求更高。为弥补塑料材质表面上有可能出现的小凹痕造成的表面缺陷，塑料外壳的表面还刻有一条条凹痕，从而赋予该产品一个垂直线条式的表面结构。这个细节设计通常被人们误解为某种后现代装饰元素，而实际上它具有明确的结构上的功能。

KF 40咖啡机问世近10年后，第3代博朗咖啡机AromaSelect系列于1993年首次亮相。博朗封闭、一体化形式的设计概念对其他咖啡机制造商的设计产生了强烈

The casing was made of a plastic that was cheaper, yet met all the technical manufacturing requirements. To compensate for possible small surface defects, the plastic was fluted, which gave it a vertical surface structure. What has often been misunderstood as some kind of post-modern decorative element had in fact a definite structural function.

In 1993, almost ten years after the KF 40, the third generation of Braun coffee machines, AromaSelect, made their first appearance. The concept of the self-contained,

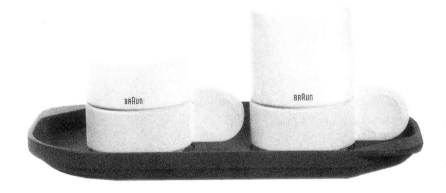

适用于一次性杯子的支撑把手与承托容器的设计研究，由经过特殊处理的纸板制成
Design study for handled holders, for disposable coffee cups, made from treated cardboard

影响，AromaSelect系列则又向前迈进了一步。该咖啡机的滤芯和玻璃壶呈双锥体形状，水箱包围机身后部，形状像一个切割过的圆筒。

20世纪90年代初，博朗的咖啡机系列产品又增加了2款意式浓缩咖啡机。其中小型的低价版本是使用蒸汽压力系统运行的，另一款较大型号的版本则是强大的水泵系统。设计这2款产品的挑战是开发出适合功能的产品形式，同时还要表达出浓缩咖啡的某些特性。较小型号的E 250 T的设备形状为圆柱体，包括安装在机身顶部带有筛网容器的柱体、玻璃壶及底座。较大型号设备的基本部件为长方体，水箱和水泵位于机身后部，它们是垂直堆叠起来的。机身前部是一个横向的长方体，这里是带有铝包层（aluminum-clad）的加热器部件。最后，滴水盘部件构成了第3个长方体。

integrative form that so strongly influenced the designs of other coffee machine manufacturers was now taken a step further. The filter element and glass jug took the form of a double cone and the water tank that was again wrapped around from the rear was shaped like a cut-out cylinder.

In the early 1990s Braun extended their coffee maker programme with two espresso machines. The smaller, low-priced version operated using a steam pressure system; the larger one with a high capacity pump system. The design challenge was to develop functionally correct product forms that also reflected the particular characteristics of espresso. The shape of the smaller appliance E 250 T is cylindrical; a column with the glass container and the sieve unit on top, sitting on a pedestal. The main elements of the larger machine were cuboids with the vertically stacked water tank and pump at the back and the aluminium-clad boiler at right angles to them. The drip tray section formed the third cube.

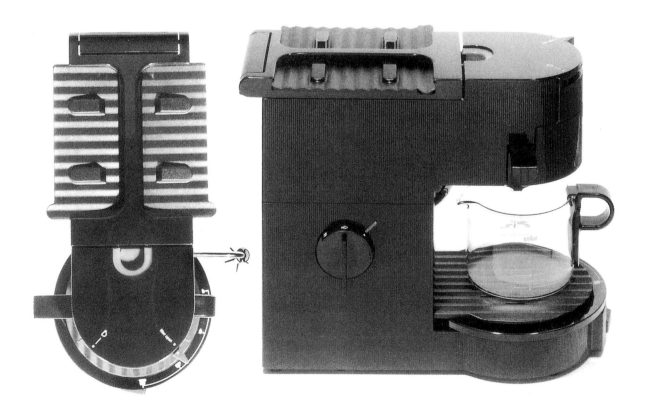

E 300意式浓缩咖啡机（1994年）
Espresso maker E 300 (1994)

左图：*Multipractic plus UK 1厨房料理机（1983年），这款机器特别适合处理少量食物*
Left: *Multipractic plus UK 1 kitchen machine (1983). This unit is specially suitable for smaller food quantities*

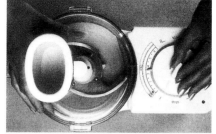

右图：*KM 32厨房料理机及其附件（1957年），这款机器适合处理大量食物*
Right: *KM 32 with accessones (1957). This machine is suitable for larger quantities*

Multipractic plus UK 1厨房料理机和vario MR 30棒式搅拌器（1981年） *Multipractic plus UK 1 kitchen machine and wand mixer vario MR 30 (1981)*

厨房用具

厨房用具是最直接意义上的工具，我们也一直将其作为工具来设计——用尽可能简单的形式和随功能变化的细节实现产品的功能实用性和一致性。厨房用具既没有花哨的装饰元素，也没有借鉴时尚潮流，因此其设计是持久的，几乎是永不过时的。KM 3/32厨房用具于1957年上市，在之后的30多年中仅对其设计细节进行了少许改动。它无疑是有史以来最长寿的工业产品之一，不过这也与当时力学的发展远没有电子学的发展迅速的事实有关。KM 3/KM 32及其之后的厨房用具都清楚地表明了完全以功能为导向的设计方案也可以具有高水平的美学质量。这源于简洁线条的相互作用，以及平衡的比例尺寸和体积关系。KM 3/KM 31还配备了一系列各种样式的附件。

Kitchen Utensils

Kitchen utensils are tools in the most direct sense of the word. And that is what we always designed them to be: consistently function-specific with the simplest forms possible and details whose form follows function. Because there were no decorative elements, there was also no fashion context and thus the designs were long-lived and almost timeless. The KM 3/32 kitchen machine came onto the market in 1957 and was produced for more than 30 years with only minor detail changes. It is undoubtedly one of the most long-lived industrial products ever. But that also naturally has something to do with the fact that the development of mechanics at this time was not anywhere near as dramatic as that of electronics. The KM 3/32 and the later kitchen appliances show clearly that a completely function-oriented design can also have a high level of aesthetic quality. This comes from the interplay of clean lines and balanced proportions and volumes. The KM 3/31 also had a comprehensive array of accessories.

K 1000多系统厨房料理机（1993年）: 带倾斜面
的电机与电源线盘的细节图
Multisystem K 1000 kitchen machine (1993):
detail of slanted motor and cable coil

K 1000多系统厨房料理机（1993年）
可装配3款不同样式的搅拌碗
Multisystem K 1000 kitchen machine (1993)with
three different bowl options

K 1000多系统厨房料理机：控制元件、搅拌碗的手柄、搅拌碗的截面图、玻璃搅拌杯、电机的截面图（细节）

Multisystem K 1000 kitchen machine: controls, grippable edge of mixing bowl, cross section of mixing bowl, glass mixer, cross section of motor (details)

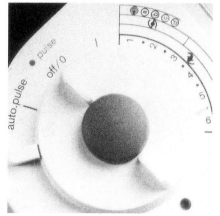
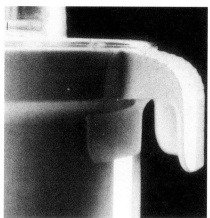
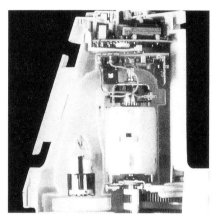

20世纪80年代初，我们开始创立新的厨房用具概念。Multipractic plus UK 1厨房料理机可在同一个主机上执行多种任务，它是一款经典的厨房搅拌机和切碎机的组合机。这台机器所搭配的不同工具都是从容器底部突出的动力装置处接入的。对于这种日常频繁使用的设备，其设计的基本要点就是要易于使用和理解、绝对安全，并且易于清洁。

In the early 1980s we began to develop a new kitchen machine concept. The Multipractic plus UK 1 allows a multitude of tasks to be performed in the same vessel. It is a classic kitchen mixer and a shredder combined. The drive for the various tools projects from the bottom of the container. Essential features belonging to this kind of appliance designed for intensive daily use are that it be easy to use and to understand, that it is completely safe and easy to clean.

1993年，博朗第3代厨房用具K 1000多功能厨房料理机上市。它的设计遵循了KM 3的基本形式，但是机身的上半部分朝向电机部分略有倾斜。这个设计细节是出于一个结构上的原因，那就是在该设备的底部还有第2台电机，它的作用是冷却主驱动电机。K 1000是一款三合一的多功能组合机，它的第1种工作方式是揉捏、搅拌和打浆，第2种工作方式是切割和擦丝，第3种工作方式是混合和切碎。每种功能都配有专门定制的适用容器—— 一个大搅拌碗、一个透明塑料罐和一个用于搅拌的玻璃容器，用以专门执行各自的功能。这台设备的大型控制元件都设置在机身顶部，用户无论是习惯用左手还是习惯用右手都能够方便地选择每项任务所需的正确速度，哪怕手指潮湿或油腻也不会影响操控。机身上的刻度符号也有助于指导用户操作。这台机器的控制装置的设计，特别是指示功能图形元素的设计，对我们来说是非常重要的。启动开关键的形式、位置及指示标签从始至终都经过细致考虑，并通过多次测试和试验反复进行优化。

In 1993, the third generation of Braun kitchen machines came onto the market – the Multisystem K 1000. The design follows the basic form of the KM 3 but with a slanting back to the motor unit. There is a structural reason for this: the bottom of the device contains a second motor that cools the main drive motor. The K 1000 is a combination of three devices in one. One work mode is kneading, stirring and beating, another is cutting and grating, and the third is mixing and chopping. Each function has its own optimised vessel tailored to the task – a large mixing bowl, a transparent plastic pot and a glass vessel for mixing. The large control element is situated at the top, allowing easy selection of the correct speed required for each task, even with wet or greasy fingers, for both left and right-handed users. The symbols on the scale also aid operation. The design of the controls, in particular the product graphics, which indicate the functions, were of great importance to us. The form, placing and labelling of switches were always thought through with great care and optimised again and again in many tests and trials.

Multiquick 350棒式搅拌器（1982年）

Multiquick 350 wand mixer (1982)

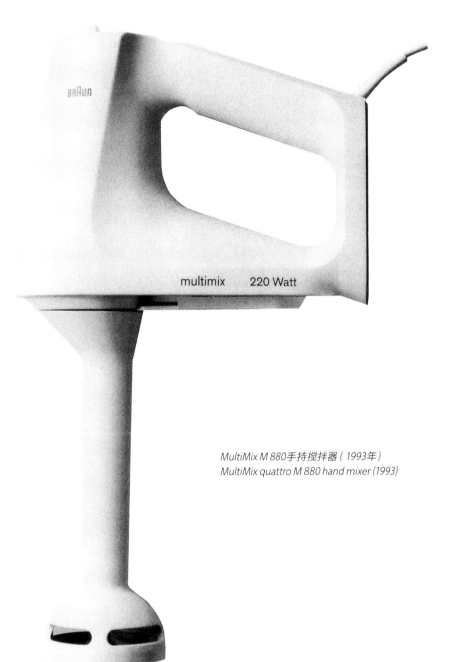

multimix 220 Watt

MultiMix M 880手持搅拌器（1993年）
MultiMix quattro M 880 hand mixer (1993)

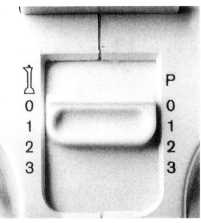

垂直安装在操作工具上方的电机部分可以直接
提供动力
*Direct power conveyance by placing the motor
vertically above the tools*

操作元件
Operating elements

手持搅拌器
Hand-held Mixers

博朗很早就开始生产棒式搅拌器，最初是在西班牙生产的。这些实用、小巧的手持工具可以让用户在要烹饪的锅中直接操作——搅拌、打泥、混合、打浆等。棒式搅拌器能实现厨房用具的许多功能，尤其适合处理少量的食材。这些设备也很容易清洁，可以直接在水龙头下冲洗。棒式搅拌器的设计基于人体工程学，因此功能结构非常合理。机身上包含电机的抓握部分经过模制成型，形成了带有易于抓握的凹槽，可以确保用户安全而轻松地操作。这个设计细节也成为后来经常被反复使用的设计方案。

另一款同样成功的产品类型就是如今几乎在每个德国家庭中都能找到的手持搅拌器，我们在20世纪60年代初设计了第一款此类设备。

Braun began producing wand mixers quite early on – initially in Spain. These practical, compact hand tools allow you to work directly in the cooking pot. Whether stirring, puréeing, mixing or beating, the wand mixer fulfils many of the tasks of a kitchen machine, especially where small quantities are concerned. They are also easy to clean by rinsing under the tap. Their design developed from ergonomic function and is therefore highly plausible. The grip area, which contains the motor, is moulded to allow safe and light handling and is a feature that has often been copied since.

An equally successful product type were the hand mixers found in almost every household these days. We designed the very first appliance of this kind at the beginning of the

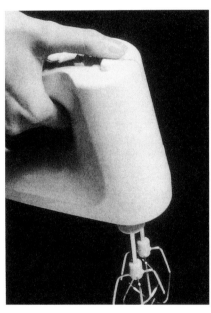

可连接不同的工具
Connection for different tools

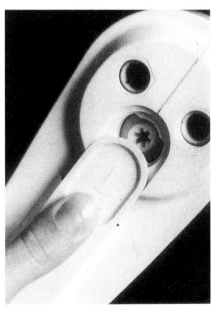

搅拌器连接处的保护片
Protection plate for mixer connection

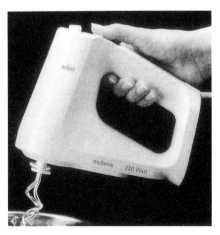

实用的抓握位置和手柄设计
Practical grip positioning and handling

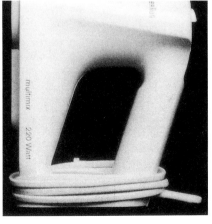

带软塑料边框的底座部分
Base with edge made of soft plastic

它有4个功能——搅拌、混合、切碎和揉捏，用户可以直接在烹饪的锅里或碗里使用它。

博朗的第1代手持搅拌器的显著特点是将电机安装在了水平方向上，这也是同时期其他同类型设备的共同特点。电机动力是以90°的直角传递给打蛋器等操作工具上。30年后，我们又重新设计了这款手持搅拌器的整体结构，使它更符合人体工程学——重量更轻，更易于抓握、操作、放置和清洁。它的设计结合了手持搅拌器和棒式搅拌器的设计经验。

1960s. It had four functions: stirring, mixing, chopping and kneading, and you could also use it directly in the pots or bowls you were cooking in.

The most significant feature of the first generation of these types of machines was the horizontal positioning of the motor. The power was transferred from it at a 90-degree angle to the tools, such as the whisks. Thirty years later we redesigned the whole guts of this mixer to allow for a more ergonomic form that was lighter and easier to grip, operate, set down and clean. This design combined the benefits of our experience with both hand mixers and wand mixers. The motor is situated vertically above the tools.

搅拌器的4种功能：搅拌、揉捏、混合、切碎
The four mixer functions: blending, kneading, mixing, shredding

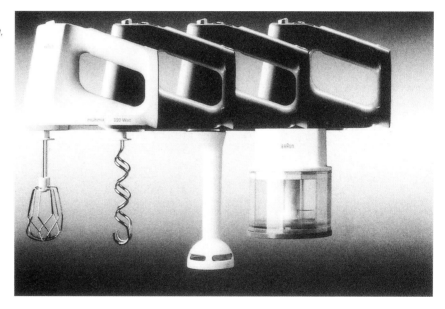

在这种手持搅拌器中，我们将电机安装在垂直于操作工具的上方，这种在垂直方向上的动力传递会使设备的动能大大增强。设备机身的平衡中心则位于操作工具的正上方，这让搅拌器拥有良好的平衡，使用户更容易用手操作。搅拌器手柄的形状既符合人体工程学，又与4种工具的操作角度正好匹配。启动开关键形状大，适于抓握，位置也便于用拇指操作。在开关键前面是一个宽大的按钮，它可以用于拆下附件工具。这款手动搅拌器还有许多实用的设计细节，如机身后部表面上带有软塑料的防滑边框，可以让搅拌器更平稳地放在湿滑的台面上。

The transfer of energy in a straight line makes the device considerably more powerful. The centre of balance lies directly above the tools, which means the mixer is well balanced and easier to guide with the hand. The grip is ergonomically formed and has just the right angle for operating each of the four types of tool. The switch is large, grippable and placed so that it is easy to operate with the thumb of the hand holding the device. In front of it is a wide button to release the tools. This hand mixer has a number of practical details, for example a border of soft plastic around the rear area so that the mixer can be put down safely on wet, slippery surfaces.

榨汁机

Juicers

博朗从一开始就非常注重食物营养并致力开发厨房用具，因此从20世纪50年代中期开始便陆续在厨房产品系列中增加了一些用于制作新鲜的果蔬汁的设备。其中，一些柑橘压榨机和榨汁机已经制造了几十年。柑橘类榨汁机MPZ 7是在后期阶段所开发的该类设备之一。它采用了早期柑橘榨汁机的基本形式，机身顶部是大压榨锥，下面是透明的果汁罐，底部是电机。果汁罐是可拆卸的，可直接将果汁倒出来。我们在1982年开发的MPZ 5柑橘压榨机也使用了这种分层结构设计，带有压榨锥的顶部也是可以直接拆卸的，便于将果汁直接倒出来。

Right from the beginning Braun was very nutrition oriented in its commitment to kitchen machines. That is why, from the mid-1950s onwards, some appliances in the programme were geared towards preparing fresh, healthy fruit and vegetable juices. Some of the citrus presses and juicers were manufactured for decades. The citrus press MPZ 7 was one of the later development phases of this kind of appliance. It follows the logical basic form of the earlier citrus presses, with the large pressing cone at the top, the transparent juice jug below and the motor at the bottom. The jug was removable for pouring the juice. The MPZ 5 citrus press from 1982 also had the same division. Here, the press at the top could be removed for pouring.

MPZ 5榨汁机（1985年）（细节）
MPZ 5 juicer (1985) (detail)

MPZ 7榨汁机 (1992年)
MPZ 7 juicer (1992)

MPZ 2榨汁机 (1972年)
MPZ 2 juicer (1972)

电熨斗

Irons

以功能为导向的优秀家电绝不意味着肤浅造作或刻意的"创新"设计，而博朗自1984年以来生产的电熨斗就是该方面很好的典范。这些产品的基本形状经受住了时间的考验，被证明是适用于电熨斗的。这里的成功之处在于我们基于这一基本形状进一步设计出了令人信服的、具有统一性和平衡性的外观，给人以柔软、轻盈、灵活的感觉。博朗的电熨斗易于握持，便于使用和操作。它与所有的博朗产品一样，开关键和相应的图形标识都是经过精心的设计和排列布局的。

Good functional design in household appliances has nothing to do with dominant or intentionally 'new' design. The Braun irons, made since 1984, are a good example of this. They have a core form that has proved its utility for years. The achievement here was to design a shape from this fundamental form that was convincingly well rounded and balanced. It comes across as being soft, light and mobile. The irons are easy to hold, use and operate. The switches and accompanying product graphics were, as with all Braun products, carefully thought through, designed and positioned.

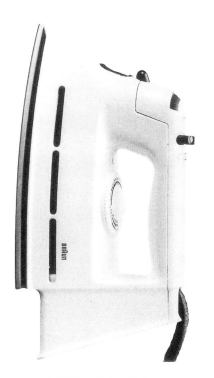

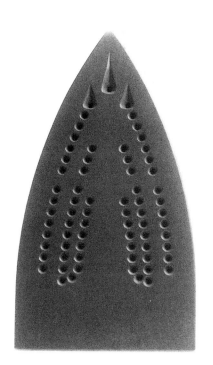

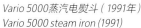

Vario 5000蒸汽电熨斗（1991年）
Vario 5000 steam iron (1991)

剃须刀

从1950年的第一款S 50剃须刀开始，所有的博朗剃须刀都具有相同的基本结构——电源装置、振动电机和剃须刀头，并且它们都是以一种合乎逻辑的结构和功能排列在一起的。S 50剃须刀的外形非常纤细，而随后开发的剃须刀产品的体型则更宽，用于突出剃须刀头的大小和性能。在这之后的40年，博朗剃须刀的技术和设计逐渐得到发展和改进，而能够像剃须刀一样以这种一致性形式持续稳定开发的工业产品并不多。设计师们也一直积极致力制订新的设计方案，改进剃须刀的功能、性能和操控性。

1985年开发的micron vario 3剃须刀首次实现了包含2种修剪系统的组合：长须修剪器位于机身上主开关的顶部，它有2个档位，用第2个档位时用户可以同时修剪短须和长须。

Shavers

From the very beginning – with the S 50 from 1950 – all Braun shavers have had the same basic construction: the main adaptor, the oscillating motor and the shaver head are all arranged on top of one another in a configuration that is a logical outcome of both construction and function. The S 50 had a very slim form. The subsequent devices were broader to accentuate the size and capacity of the shaver head. Over the following 40 years the technology and design of the Braun shavers were gradually developed and improved. There are probably very few industrial products that have been worked on with such consistency in this way. The designers were always involved in developing new solutions for improving the function, performance characteristics and handling of the shaver.

One example is the combination of the two cutting systems that first appeared in the micron vario 3 from 1985. The long hair trimmer is at the top by the main switch and can be extended in two settings. The second setting allows both short and longer hairs to be cut at the same time.

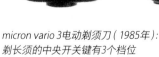

micron vario 3电动剃须刀（1985年）：
剃长须的中央开关键有3个档位

micron vario 3 electric shaver (1985):
The central switch for cutting long hair has three positions

设计micron vario 3剃须刀的过程中，设计团队的一项重要任务是设计产品图标，使它能够突出产品的新功能。剃须刀的另一个改良之处是外壳表面的创新设计：它由硬塑料和软塑料组合而成，并采用了双注射成型生产工艺。我们为了找到合适的外壳材料及其制造技术，与一家塑料生产商进行了密切合作和长期深入的测

Here as well an important task for the design team was devising the product graphics that indicated the new functions. Another example is the innovative design of the appliance's surface, made from a combination of hard and sort plastics produced using a double injection procedure. It took many long and intense experiments with a plastics producer to come up with suitable materials and the right

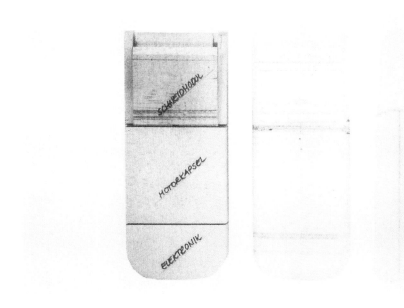

有助于研究电动剃须刀（micron vario 3）结构细节的模型机
Models help to study construction details of the electric shaver (micron vario 3).

剃须刀外壳：软塑料和硬塑料的组合（细节图）
Shaver housing: a combination of soft and plastics (detail)

左图：用于拆卸剃须箔的各种设计备选方案
Left: Various design options for removing shaving foils
右图：主开关的各种设计备选方案
Right: Design options for the main switch

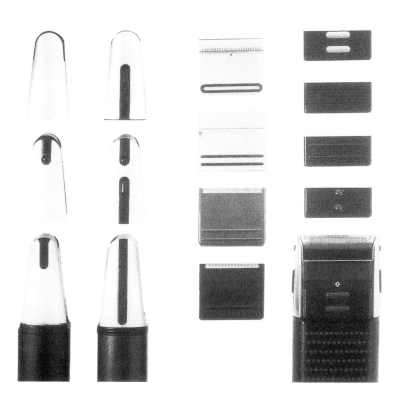

micron vario 3通用电动剃须刀（1988年）
micron vario 3 universal electric shaver (1988)

试。1979年推出的micron plus剃须刀是第一款采用硬塑料外壳和软抓握凸起纹理表面的剃须刀。这种设计方案在用户使用过程中具有相当大的优势，它可以使剃须刀握起来更舒适，也可以确保放下剃须刀时不会从光滑的台面滑落。后来，我们还将这种软硬材质结合的技术应用在了博朗许多其他的设备上。

manufacturing technology. The micron plus from 1979 was the first shaver to feature a hard plastic shell with a soft grip dot-textured surface. This solution had considerable advantages during use: the shaver was agreeably comfortable to hold and it did not slide off slippery surfaces when it was put down. We went on to implement this hard-soft technology in a number of other appliances. A third example for the design/construction

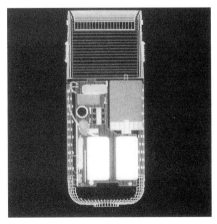

内部结构：micron vario 3电动剃须刀

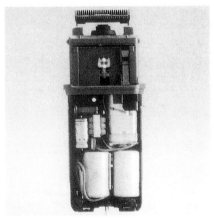

Construction: micron vario 3 electric shaver

博朗关于创造性结构设计的第3个例子是Flex control剃须刀（1991年）的灵活剃须刀头，它带有可以来回摆动的双重切割箔，能够更好地贴合面部轮廓。这款摆动式剃须刀头由于机械结构复杂，因此只有在技术人员和设计师的密切合作下才能同时实现有效的功能性和紧凑的外观。

aspect of our design is the flexible shaver head of the Flex control (1991). It had double cutting foils and could swing back and forth to better fit the contours of the face. Because of the difficult mechanics involved in a flexible shaver head, the final functional and compact form was only realisable thanks to very close collaboration between the technicians and the designers.

Flex Control 4550电动剃须刀（1991年），带摆动头
Flex Control 4550 electric shaver (1991) with swing head

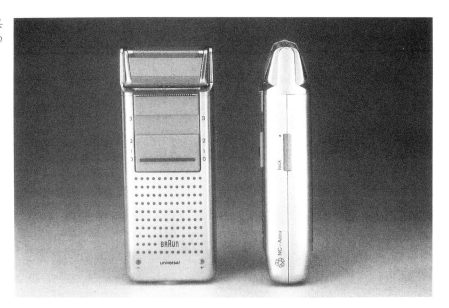

exact 5胡须修剪器（1986年）
exact 5 beard trimmer (1986)

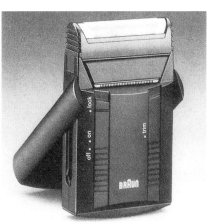

电池供电的袖珍豪华旅行者剃须刀（1990年）
Battery-powered pocket de luxe traveller shaver (1990)

面向日本市场的Dual Aqua干湿两用电动剃须刀（1987年）
Dual Aqua electrical shaver for Japan (1987)

吹风机和美发造型器

关于吹风机设计的故事其实也是关于吹风机手柄设计的故事。经典的吹风机手柄一般是与气流方向成直角的。然而，我们通过更仔细的研究发现，这种垂直的手柄握法对于用户烘干自己的头发并不是特别合适。

Hairdryers and Hairstylers

The story of hairdryer design of is also the story of handle design. The classic hairdryer's handle is at right angles to the direction of the air current. Yet a closer examination told us that this perpendicular grip is not particularly practical for drying your own hair.

P 1500/PE 1500吹风机（1981年）
P 1500 / PE 1500 blow dryer (1981)

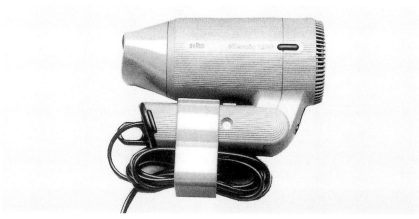

PA 1250 travelcombi旅行可折叠式手柄吹风机（1985年）
PA 1250 travelcombi travel blow dryer with foldable handle (1985)

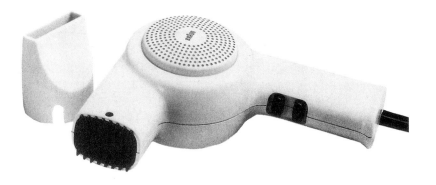

HLD 1000/PG 1000吹风机（1975年）
HLD 1000 / PG 1000 blow dryer (1975)

实际上，手柄与气流的角度更小的吹风机才更容易使用，用起来也不那么累。因此，我们开发了手柄更符合人体工程学的吹风机。现在，这种手柄设计方案已成为同类产品的标准配置。针对旅行吹风机，我们则设计了可以折叠至机身处的手柄。

A hairdryer with a more acutely angled handle, however, is much easier, less inhibiting and less tiring to use. The result was hairdryers with ergonomically angled handles – a configuration that has since become the norm everywhere. For travelling versions, we designed a handle that could fold against the body of the machine.

多年来，我们开发了各种多功能的头发护理用具。

Over the years we developed a broad and versatile programme of hair care appliances.

其中，要特别提到使用丁烷气体驱动而非电加热驱动的卷发器。这项新技术是博朗于1982年首次推出的。这种免插电设备的优势在于可以随时随地使用。

A special mention should be give to the curling tongs that were heated using butane gas rather than with electricity. Braun first unveiled this new technology in 1982. These electricity-free appliances had the advantage in that they can could be used anywhere and any time.

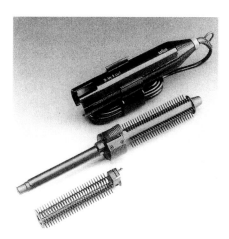

TCC 30卷发刷和卷发夹
TCC 30 curling brush and curler

GCC丁烷驱动卷发器（1988年）
GCC butane-powered curler（1988）

LS 34卷发棒(1988年)
LS 34 curler iron（1988）

牙齿和口腔护理

Dental Care

像博朗的许多其他产品系列一样，牙刷和口腔冲洗器也表现出明显的设计一致性。博朗于1991年推出的Plak Control电动牙刷虽然具有创新的技术，但基本上保留了其前身产品的实用的基础样式。

Like many other Braun product lines, the toothbrushes and oral irrigators demonstrated a distinctive degree of design consistency. The Plak Control electric toothbrush introduced in 1991 had innovative technology, yet

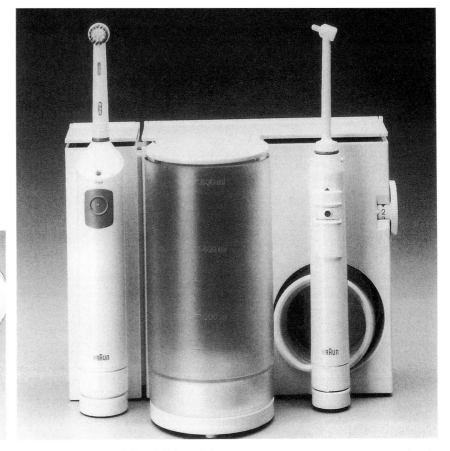

摆动式旋转牙刷头
Oscillating rotary brush

Plak Control OC 5545S牙齿护理套装（1992年） Plak Control OC 5545S dental care centre (1992)

这款牙刷的圆形刷头展示了博朗设计师的核心理念，即产品的整体质量是许多精心设计的细节的总和。牙刷刷头需要以3000次每分钟的频率来回摆动才能去除牙菌斑，为此技术人员采用了一个小角齿轮。设计师首先尝试将小角齿轮密封起来以避免其与牙膏接触而磨损，但是添加了密封件的结构意味着牙刷无法像实际需要的那样紧凑小巧，无法在口腔内适度地来回移动。于是，设计师和技术人员提出了一个解决方案——使用由烧结耐磨钢制成的齿轮，这样做既不需要密封件，还可以保证刷头非常小。虽然这是一个毫米级的构造细节，但是它对用户体验和设计却具有决定性的作用。

essentially retained the practical basic form of its predecessor.

This toothbrush's rounded brush head is proof of the Braun designers' core beliefs that the quality of the whole is the sum of many well-solved details. To free the teeth from plaque, the brush head oscillates back and forth at 3,000 times per minute. A small right-angled drive was used for this that the technicians tried hard to insulate from the toothpaste since it acted like sand and quickly wore the gears out. Yet this insulation would have meant that the toothbrush could not have been as compact as it needed to be to move around easily within the mouth. So the designers and the technicians came up with a solution together: a gear mechanism made from vitrified, abrasion-proof steel that needs no insulation and can also be very small. That was design on a millimetre scale that was as decisive for the user as it was for the design quality.

Plak Control 可去除牙菌斑电动牙刷（1994年）
Plak Control plaque removal set (1994)

时钟与袖珍计算器

自16世纪彼得·亨莱因（Peter Henlein）小巧的装饰钟表"纽伦堡蛋"（Nuremburg Egg）问世以来，私人随身携带钟表的装饰性和象征性远超实用性，但博朗却一直将时钟视为测量时间的工具。因此，这使得博朗的钟表拥有了独有的风格特点，这意味着人们总是可以一目了然地分辨出博朗制造的旅行闹钟或手表。这并不是因为它们有什么外形上的特点，恰恰相反，正是因为它们完全没有那些外形特点。要知道，博朗的设计只关注时钟的唯一功能——报时。

Clocks and Pocket Calculators

Since Peter Henlein's Nuremburg Egg from the 16th century, clocks for private use have tended to be decorative and representative rather than functional. At Braun, on the other hand, we have always regarded them as instruments for measuring time. They acquired their particular character – which meant you could always tell a Braun travel alarm clock or watch at a glance – not from formal peculiarities but, quite the opposite, from a complete lack of them. The design focused purely on the single function of a clock: to tell the time.

funktional 桌面闹钟（1975年）
funktional table and alarm clock (1975)

左图：phase 3闹钟（1972年）
Left: phase 3 alarm clock (1972)
右图：ABK 30墙面挂钟（1982年）
Right: ABK 30 wall clock (1982)

DB 10 fsl数字时钟收音机（1991年）
time control DB 10 fsl digital clock radio（1991）

　　最早的博朗电子时钟之一是1975年上市的funktional闹钟，它的主要特点是有一个大的、倾斜的、显示数字时间的LED显示器，还有一个向外凸起的、易于使用的操控按钮。而在随后的几年里，我们生产了许多带有钟表盘模拟显示器的时钟。这是因为相对于数字显示方式，人们更偏爱更清晰、更舒适的钟表盘时间显示方式。博朗的钟表盘也是经过精心设计的，以尽可能地清晰、易读。

One of the first Braun electronic clocks was the funktional alarm clock that came on the market in 1975. Its main feature was the large, angled digital LED time display and the accentuated, easy-to-use buttons. In later years a number of clocks with analogue displays were produced that were clearer and more comfortable to read for most people. The clock faces were designed with the greatest imaginable care to be as clear and easy to read as possible.

ABR 21时钟收音机（1978年）
ABR 21 clock radio（1978）

ET 88 world traveller时钟计算器（1991年）：它的按键是凸起的，以确保操作起来更容易、更准确
ET 88 calculator and clock world traveller (1991): Keys are convex to ensure better and more accurate operation

AW 15/20/30/50手表（1989—1994年）
AW 15/20/30/50 wristwatches(1989–1994)

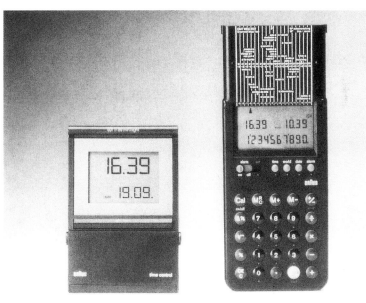

DB 10 fsl时钟与world traveller时钟计算器。在这两款设备的设计中，产品的图形设计是重中之重

The time control DB 10 fsl clock and the world traveller ET 88 calculator and clock combination. The product graphics were of primany importance in the design of both devices.

从1976年起，袖珍计算器也成为博朗产品计划的一部分，它们遵循了与博朗其他产品类似的设计原则。虽然计算器产品在技术上是不断发展的，但它们的外观在20年内基本保持不变。袖珍计算器的尺寸使它们刚好可以被轻松地拿在手中；计算器的按键排列得非常清楚，凸起的按键设计还向用户传达了一种心理上的暗示——可以更容易、更准确地键入。

From 1976 on, pocket calculators were also part of the Braun programme and they followed similar principles. They were being constantly technically developed, yet their design remained more or less constant for two decades. The pocket calculators' dimensions allowed them to sit easily in the hand. The keypads were clearly organised. The keys' convex curves served a psychological function in that they were simply easier to press accurately.

设计研究

博朗的设计部门在进行日常工作的同时一直积极参与产品的自主设计研究。我认为，设计师拥有萌发和完善自己的想法的创意空间是非常重要的。由于各种原因，我们的大多数设计研究从未投入生产，但它们却为新产品开发和我们的常规设计工作提供了巨大的推动力。以下将为大家展示的是我们的一些研究案例，如时钟、便携式设备、高保真系统、时钟收音机和手电筒，以及其他未曾展示的研究项目，不只是现有产品的外形修改，还有针对全新产品的概念性设计。在研究过程中，我们经常使用在当时属于完全创新的技术或者试图预测未来的技术发展情况。

我们的研究项目的设计和最终形式都是从效用最优化的角度出发的，这一点与我们那些已开发的产品并没有什么不同。针对时钟收音机的2项研究就是很好的例证。

Design Studies

The Braun design department was always involved in self-initiated design studies alongside the usual daily workload. I believe it is very important for designers to have the creative space to develop and refine their own ideas. Most of our studies never went into production-for various reasons-but they often gave important impulses to product development and our regular design work. A few examples are shown on the followting pages-clocks, portables, hi-fi systems, clock radios and flashlights. The studies shown, and those not shown, were not simply formal modifications to existing products, but designs for totally new object concepts. We often used completely innovative technologies or attempted to anticipate future technological developments.

Our studies were no different from our realised products in that the designs and the resulting forms always evolved from an optimisation of utility. The two studies for clock radios show this well.

研究：电池与太阳能板相结合的时钟收音机
Study: battery and solar-powered clock radio

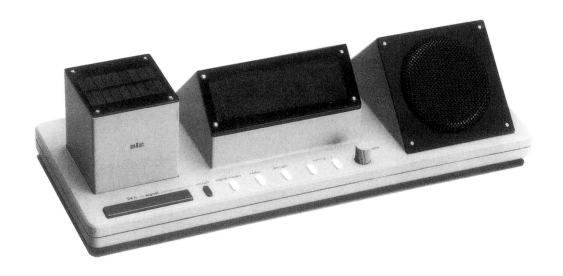

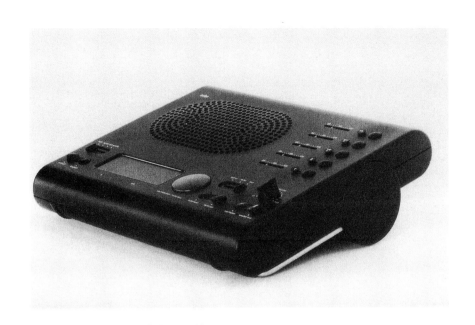

研究：带盒式磁带组件的模块化时钟
收音机系统（1978年）
Study: Modular clock radio system
with cassette deck (1978)

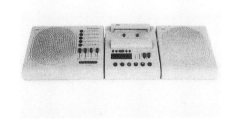

便携式音响系统（1978年）研究：
在设备控制面板的前面有一个可滑动
的斜面扬声器

Portable music system(1978) study:
One speaker slides in front of the control panel

便携式音响组合研究：将扬声器推开，露出内部的控制面板
Portable music combination study: The speaker is pushed aside to reveal the control panel

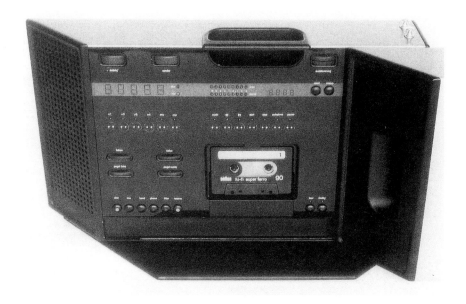

第98页所展示的时钟收音机由电池和太阳能共同供电，这是因为光靠太阳能供电无法使用这台设备。这个设计强调了添加性：3个简单几何形状的设备彼此之间明显分开，它们被安装在一个包含了电路板和操作功能按键的公共操作台上。左边的立方体含有电池组件，中间的棱镜体构成了太阳能元件，而右边的棱镜体则构成了扬声器。

第99页所展示的时钟收音机是模块化和集成式的。它有3个模块：时钟收音机、盒式磁带播放机及附加扬声器。这3个模块共同构成了一个同质的组合体。

The design on page 98 proposed an object powered by both batteries and solar energy-solar energy alone would not have been sufficient to run the appliance. The design is emphatically additive – three simple geometric forms, clearly separated from one another, sit on a shared tablet containing the circuit board and the operating functions. The cube on the left contains the battery, the central cut-off prism form the solar element, and the prism on the right the loudspeakers.

The clock radio on page 99 is both modular and integrative. It has three modules – a radio plus clock, a cassette player and an additional loudspeaker – that together form a homogenous unit.

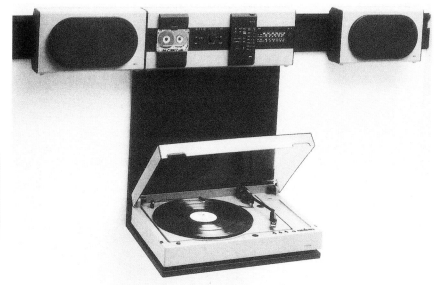

用户友好型支撑件设置
User-friendly placement of the support

沿轨道安装在墙壁上

Wall-mounted on a rail

带有远程遥控的 "telecompakt" 高保真系统的研究（1979年）
Study for a 'telecompakt' hi-fi system with remote control (1979)

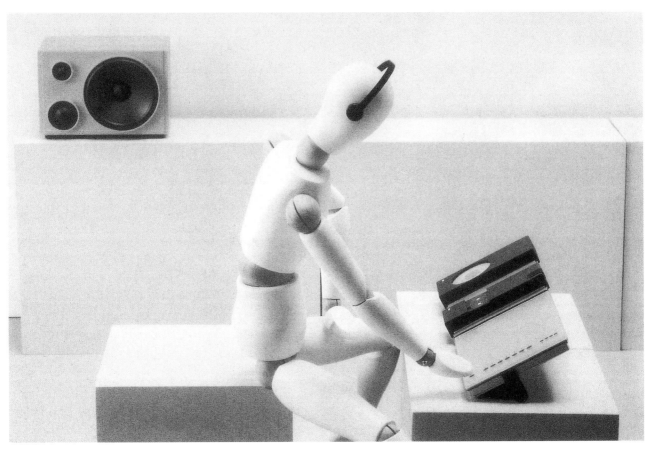

对Audio Additiv Programm高保真音响系统的
研究（1979年）

Study for the 'Audio Additiv Programm' hi-fi
system (1979)

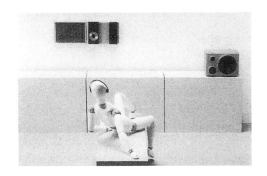

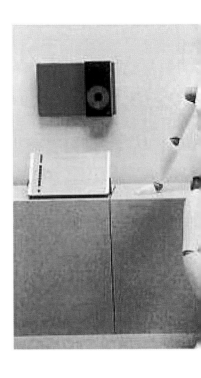

这3个模块单元机也可以分别单独使用。这套系统的设计目的是开发出一款功能强大的收音机设备。这个设计已经预见了未来将出现的迷你立体声音响系统的概念。

The three modules can also be used separately. The intention was to develop a high-capacity radio. The resulting design was a forerunner of the concept of miniaturised stereo systems.

第99页和第100页展示了一种便携式音响系统的设计，这款产品可以完全折叠闭合，因此便于携带。设备的斜边由抗冲击的柔软材料制成，用户在使用的时候，只需将包含了第2个扬声器的前部滑动装置滑到一侧，就会露出内部的操作元件。安装在侧面的第2个扬声器增加了设备的底座面积，进而提高了音质效果。

Pages 99 and 100 show a design for a portable stereo system that can be completely folded closed for transport. The angled sides are made of soft, impact-resistant material. To use, you slide the front part, containing the second loudspeaker, to one side to reveal the operating unit. The second, side-mounted loudspeaker expands the speaker base and thereby improves the sound quality.

20世纪70年代末，我们对高保真系统进行了大量研究，其中一个概念设计的项目名称为 "telecompackt"（第101页）。这是一个非常紧凑的模块化音响系统，它的特别之处是由遥控器来操控，这在当时是非常新颖的。立体声音响组件被设计成立式，同时还搭配了一个专门开发的安装轨道，这个轨道可以将设备电线隐藏起来，并使 "telecompackt" 设备可以悬挂在墙壁上。这个音响系统中还包含一台磁带播放机，因为当时CD光盘还没有流行起来。如果需要的话，在这套组合设备中还可以添加博朗的其他任意一款唱片机，如PDS 550等。

Towards the end of the 1970s we did a number of studies for hi-fi systems. One of these concepts had the working title 'telecompakt' (page 101). It was a very compact modular stereo system that specifically relied on a remote control – which was new in those days. The stereo components were designed to be stand-alone, but there was also a specially developed track that could conceal the cables and enabled the 'telecompakt' to be hung on the wall. The system had a cassette player – CDs had not yet been invented. Any record player from the Braun programme, such as the PDS 550, could be added on if required.

对Audio Additiv Programm设备上的扬声器和扩音器的研究
speaker and amplifier for the 'Audio Additiv Programme' study

带有大显示屏的控制和操作元件
Control and operating elements on a large display

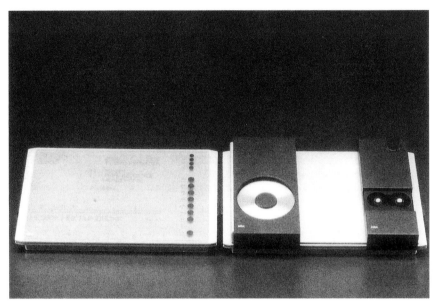

博朗在20世纪70年代末的第2项重要研究是"Audio Additiv Programm"系统（第102—104页）。这个产品系统的概念设计使用了早期的微处理器技术，这个技术后来在整个高保真行业的发展中起到了决定性作用。

微处理器技术可使各个组件通过共享数据线来实现相互通信，这让设计在产品组合和功能区分方面有了更大的自由度。因此，设计师可以将扩音器和扬声器组合在一个功能模块中，然后再将所有的控制和操作元件组合在第2个模块中。

A second important study from the end of the 1970s was the 'Audio Additiv Programm' (pages 102–104). This system concept used early microprocessor technology, which later came to play a decisive role in the development of the entire hi-fi industry.

The microprocessors allowed the individual components to communicate with one another via a shared data bus. This allowed greater freedom in combining and differentiating functions. The amplifier and speakers could thus be combined in a single performance module. A second module then combined all the control and operating elements.

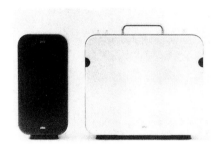

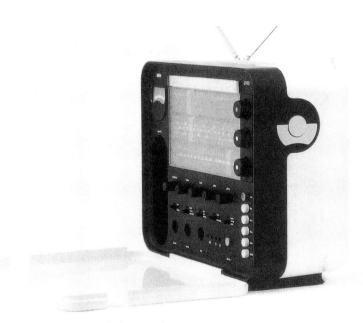

对带有独立扬声器的世界波段收音机的研究（1970年）

Study for a world receiver with separate loudspeakers (1970)

这个系统还可以包含其他模块，如盒式磁带机和CD播放机等。每个模块单元机都使用了相同的基本外壳——由压铸锌制成的外盒。这套产品系统的外观设计展示了其高科技含量和新颖性。设备的控制和操作元件与现在的笔记本电脑的类似，即在大显示屏上，有关功能的信息一目了然，便于用户从远处阅读。设备上面的传感器按钮及远程控制装置都可供用户操作。这套系统中的各个模块单元机可以根据需求进行任意组合。这套系统就像我们其他的大多数研究一样，在一定程度上预见了音响系统未来的发展。在技术上，该

Further modules were, for example, the cassette deck and the CD player. The same basic casing was used for each element: a die-cast zinc frame. The system's design communicates both its high-tech qualities and its novelty. The control and operating elements were precursors of today's laptops: A large display, visible from a distance, gives the user clear information about the functions. Sensor buttons, as well as a remote control device, were intended for its operation. The individual modules could be arranged in any constellation imaginable. As with most of our studies, this device predicted the future to a certain extent. Today, some 30 years later, it is

迷你型世界收音机的研究（1978年）
Study for a miniaturised world receiver (1978)

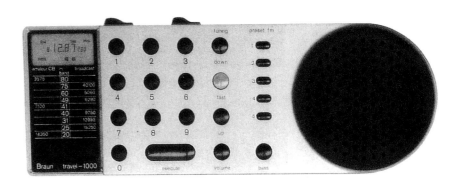

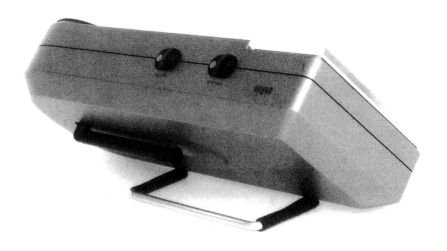

系统的许多方面在如今看来自然是有些过时的，但它仍然令人印象深刻。

第105页和第106页展示了博朗关于世界收音机的2项研究。凭借1963年开发的T 1000设备，博朗创造了权威性的高性能便携式无线电收音机，并将其命名为"世界收音机"。多年后，我们又开展了另一项研究（第105页），该设备带有一个自身集成的扬声器和一两个附加的独立扬声器，可以显著提高音质。在这个研究中，我们打算替换掉早期T 1000设备的金属外壳，计划采用双层的塑料外壳。而在后来的一项研究中（第106页），我们则利用了更先进的微电子技术开发了一种与早期袖珍收音机尺寸相当的高性能世界收音机。

我们还有一个鲜为人知的、未实现的外部项目研究案例，它是一个市政时钟，当时的计划是将它安装在法兰克福的一个城市广场上。它细长中心柱的横截面是三角形的，钟体顶部的倾斜面设计有助于突出时钟形状，并为太阳能板提供了采光平面。

naturally technically outdated in many aspects, but it is impressive nonetheless.

The images on pages 105 and 106 show two studies for the 'world receiver'. With the T 1000 from 1963, Braun created the definitive high-performance portable radio receiver as well as the name 'world receiver'. Years later we developed another study for an appliance (p. 105) that had an integrated loudspeaker for voice and one, or two, additional speakers for considerably improved music reproduction quality. Here, instead of the T 1000 metal housing, a double shelled plastic housing was planned. A further study later on (p. 106) used the more advanced miniaturisation of microelectronics to develop a higher-performance world receiver that was the size of the earlier pocket receivers.

Another, less known, example of our unrealised studies and external projects was that of a civic clock, which was to be erected in one of Frankfurt's town squares. The slim central column with a triangular cross-section had a slanting top, which helped emphasise the form and provided a surface for solar panels.

对与RT 20桌面收音机（第25页）类似的Tischsuper收音机的研究（1961年）
Study for Tischsuper (1961) similar to RT20 (page 25)

对公共广场市政时钟的研究（1988年）
Study for a clock for a public square (1988)

博朗Manulux手持式手电筒（1940年）：德国战时和战后的重要产品，它不含电池，仅供民用。截至1948年，其产量已达数百万只
Hand dynamo flash light 'Manulux' (1940): An important product during the war and postwar period, without battery for civilian use only. Millions of them were produced up until 1948

对燃气手电筒的研究

Study for a gas-powered flashlight

　　在1940年之后的几年里，博朗制造了一款手电筒，它需要用户操控一个大按钮来启动内置发电机为其供电。许多年后，我们又研究了使用更不寻常的技术的自供电手电筒，它的电力装置与博朗的另一款使用丁烷筒提供燃料的卷发器类似。我们在这项研究中还使用了现代的白炽煤气罩（Gas mantle）作为光源。

　　紧凑型桌面台灯（第109页上部图片）的研究也涉及了高效能源和新技术，它的光源使用了当时最新研发的冷光节能灯泡。

During the years following 1940, Braun produced a torch with user-generated electricity to power it. By operating a large button you could set the dynamo in motion. Many years later we investigated the idea of a batteryless torch again with much more unusual technology. This version was to be powered in a similar manner to the gas-fuelled Braun hair curling tongs – with butane cartridges. The light source was to be a modern version of the gas mantle.

The study for the compact desk lamp (p. 109 top) was also concerned with energy efficiency and new technologies. The light source for this was to be the energy-saving cold light bulb that had recently been developed.

我们也一直致力时钟与收音机组合设备的设计研究。其中的2项研究参见第99页，第3项研究参见本页。在第3项设计案例中，时钟和收音机被视为是通过紧固件连接起来的2个独立模块。我们基于对未

We worked again and again on designs for clock-radio combinations. Two of these studies are pictured on page 99 and a third on page 109. In this case the clock and radio were concieved as separate modules connected by a fastener. In anticipation of

可调节的水平固定式台灯的设计研究（1976年）
Design study for a table lamp with flexible horizontal table fixing (1976)

节能灯泡台灯的研究（1975年）

Study for a table lamp for energy saving light bulbs (1975)

数字收音机与时钟组合的研究（1974年）

Study for a digital radio-clock combination (1974)

首次研究用于搭配博朗剃须刀的化妆品

First study for cosmetics to complement the Braun shaver

来技术发展的预期，将数字显示器设计为类似于LED屏幕的点阵格栅。这款时钟与收音机的组合设备也可以安装在墙面上。

自20世纪50年代以来，博朗还生产了各种风扇型暖风机。第1款是带有圆柱形切向风扇的紧凑型H1暖风机。后来，博朗还生产了带有传统径向风扇的暖风机。我们通过对上述暖风机的研究发现，风扇的片层布置方式也可以将气流导向侧面，因此无须额外添加让整个风扇侧向移动的附加装置。

later technical developments, the digit display was designed like an LED dot matrix field. This clock-radio combination could also be wall-mounted.

From the 1950s onwards, Braun also manufactured fan heaters. The first was the compact model H 1 with a cylindrical tangential fan. Later Braun also produced heaters with traditional radial fans. The study above shows a fan whose lamellae are arranged so that the air current can also be directed to the side, thus rendering a mechanism for side-to-side movement of the whole fan unnecessary.

为汉莎航空公司设计的产品

1983—1984年，汉莎航空公司邀请我们参加关于飞机乘客餐具的创新设计竞赛，这意味着我们要与另一位设计师沃尔夫·卡内格尔（Wolf Karnagel）竞争，航空公司最终采纳了后者的设计方案。在这个竞赛中，机上餐具的设计必须满足3个要求：首先是重量要最轻，其次是要根据3种不同等级的机舱进行差异化设计，最后是成本要最低。当时，我们开发了一系列强调功能性的餐具，3套餐具的设计极具一致性。在竞赛过程中，我们制订了一些创新性的设计解决方案。

Designed for Lufthansa

Between 1983 and 1984 Lufthansa commissioned us to develop designs for new onboard tableware. For this we competed with another designer (Wolf Karnagel), who eventually won the commission. The on-board tableware had a number of requirements to fulfil: minimal weight was critical, three clearly distinguished sets for the three different classes on board and, cost minimisation. We developed a range of tableware that stressed functionality, and the versions for the three classes were very homogenous. During our work we came up with a number of innovative solutions.

例如，我们提出了杯子使用合成把手的方案，即用化学方法将把手焊接在瓷器上，这是我们在设计咖啡机时采用的一项创新技术。它的优点是手柄不发热，杯体的造价更低，杯子的整体重量也更轻。

For example, we proposed synthetic handles for the cups, which were chemically welded to the porcelain – a technology that we had explored for our coffee makers. The advantages were that the handle did not get hot, the manufacture of the cup body was cheaper and the cup as a whole was lighter.

111

为吉列集团下属公司进行的设计研究

In 1974年，我们受邀为缤乐美（Paper Mate）公司设计了一套书写工具。缤乐美公司是吉列集团旗下的一家子公司，多年来一直生产书写工具。我们为其开发了2个版本的书写工具，它们的操作机制各不相同。

在第1个版本中，笔芯是通过压力向前推出的。而在第2个版本中，笔芯是通过转动笔杆中心一个凸起的元件向前推出的。我们还设计了一种新型的笔尖密封结构，可以保持毛毡笔尖不干燥。这里特别值得一提的是我们关于笔夹的设计。在第1个版本中，笔杆侧边的笔夹是可拆卸的。而在第2个版本中，笔夹与笔杆几乎是齐平的，用户可以通过轻轻按压这个具有弹力的笔夹顶部来打开笔夹。

Design Studies for Companies Belonging to the Gillette Group

In 1974 we did some designs for a set of writing implements commissioned by Paper Mate, a company belonging to the Gillette group, that has manufactured writing implements for many years. Two versions were developed, which differed in their operating mechanism.

In the first version the pencil leads were pushed forward using pressure, in the second by turning a ridged central element. A new kind of sealing mechanism at its tip protected the felt-tip pen from drying out. Particular attention was paid to the clips, which were removable in the version with the pressure mechanism. In the second version they were almost flush with the pen body and could be opened with spring pressure.

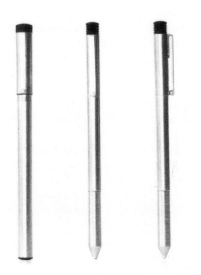

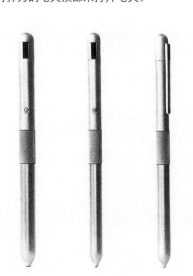

博朗的设计团队首先是为博朗工作，但也不是只为博朗工作，也可以承接数量有限的外部委托项目。多年来，博朗为吉列集团的姊妹公司嘉芙瑞公司、欧乐B公司，以及为赫斯特（Hoechst AG）化学品公司和西门子（Siemens）公司等其他外部公司都开发了一些设计项目。

The Braun design team worked first and foremost for Braun, but not exclusively. It was able to take on a limited number of external commissions as well. Thus, over the years, a number of designs were developed for Braun's sister companies within the Gillette corporation including Jafra and Oral-B as well as other companies such as Hoechst AG and Siemens.

为嘉芙瑞公司设计的化妆品包装（1992年）
Designs for Jafra cosmetics (1992)

其中一个特别有趣的、设计要求高且成功实现的项目是为嘉芙瑞公司开发的产品包装及对该公司的概念设计。这家公司的总部位于加利福尼亚州，主要生产皮肤友好型的高品质化妆品，当时正计划在全球范围内扩大市场。我们的包装设计源于对该产品及其竞争产品的详尽研究和分析。这个项目之所以成功，其决定性因素就是博朗的设计原则可以在这样一个通常由时尚风潮主控的设计领域中顺畅地展开。我们为嘉芙瑞公司的化妆品量身定制了一套优雅、现代、吸引女性的独立包装，这款包装的开发设计同样源自与博朗技术设备设计相同的基本原则和设计精神。

An especially interesting, demanding and successful project was the development of a packaging and corporate design concept for Jafra. This California-based company manufactures high-quality, skin-friendly cosmetics and was planning a worldwide expansion of their market at the time. Our packaging design resulted from exhaustive studies and competition analysis. The decisive factor was that Braun design principles could be implemented without limitation in an area that is usually governed by fashionable, literally 'cosmetic', design. We developed an elegant, product-relevant, contemporary and completely self-contained packaging design for Jafra that also appealed to women. It came from the same basic principles and the same spirit that governed the design of Braun's technical appliances.

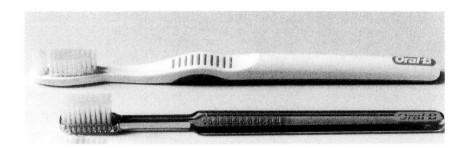

为欧乐B公司设计的牙刷
Toothbrushes for Oral-B

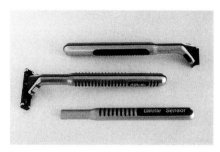

吉列传感剃须刀
Gillette sensor razor

欧乐B公司是一家重要的牙科护理产品制造商，牙刷是它的主要产品之一。欧乐B公司与嘉芙瑞公司一样，也是吉列集团下属的一家公司。

牙刷的设计重点是手柄要符合人体工程学，即让用户尽可能轻松、安全地握住牙刷。为了实现这一目标，我们使用了软塑料和硬塑料相结合的组合材质方案，这是我们多年前在开发博朗剃须刀外壳时所采用的方案。具体的制造技术就是使这两种材料在同一个注射过程中黏合在一起。

为博朗的其他合作公司开发的设计项目

我们还为赫斯特化学品公司设计了一款用于为糖尿病患者注射胰岛素的注射器，它的电子元件可以精确地设定注射剂量。我们的设计任务则是开发出一个方便、紧凑、易于使用的日常设备。

我们为注射器选择了截面为椭圆形的笔杆形状。

The toothbrushes are products for Oral-B, an important manufacturer of dental care products that, like Jafra, was a company belonging to Gillette.

The main task with the toothbrushes was the natural and ergonomic design of the grip. You should be able to hold the brush as lightly and securely as possible. To achieve this we used a combination of soft and hard plastics that we had developed years before for the casings of Braun shavers. The two materials were combined within the same injection process.

Design for Companies Associated with Braun

For Hoechst AG we designed a device for diabetics to inject their own insulin. An electronic component allowed exact calibration of the dose. Our task was to develop a handy, compact, easy-to-use device for daily use.

We decided upon a simple pen shape with an oval cross-section.

为赫斯特化学品公司设计的注射器
Injection device commissioned by Hoechst AG

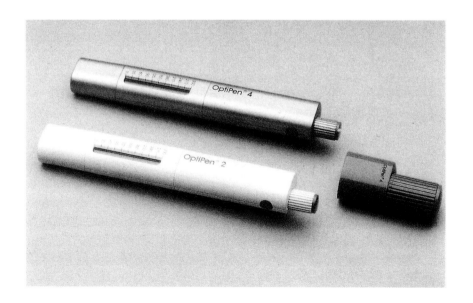

注射器的底部由富有弹性的软塑料制成，因此特别容易抓握。而注射器的顶部则为硬塑料材质，带有明显的拇指状凹陷，上面凸起的棱条则是由软塑料制成的。

The underside was made of soft, and therefore particularly easy to grip, plastic. The upper side was hard plastic with a distinct thumb-shaped depression that had raised ribs made of softer material.

为西门子公司设计的电话
Telephone for Siemens

就西门子电话的设计而言，是当时的技术限制了设计方案。于是，我们将注意力集中在设计出一个清晰排列的操作面板上，并为电话听筒安排了向外倾斜的位置。这一创新的解决方案让用户可以更加轻松地使用左手拿起听筒，而不必扭转手腕。

In the case of the Siemens telephone, we had to work with existing technology, which limited the design possibilities. We concentrated on a clearly arranged control panel and suggested an angled position for the handset. This innovative solution allows you to pick up the handset with your left hand without having to twist it.

教学

Teaching

我于1981—1997年在汉堡美术学院任教，同时也担任博朗设计部门的主管。我认为在汉堡的教学工作对我而言既是一个机会也是一种责任。我深信好的设计始于培养出好的设计师。

我发现德国设计方面的教学质量并不高，而其中一个主要原因就是院校数量过多，但大多数学校无法为工业设计师提供满足其在当今和未来实践中所需的高水平设计要求的教学内容。因此，我想在这里展示一些由我的学生设计而不是我设计的作品，正如我在博朗的设计团队所设计的许多产品也不是我设计的一样。不过，它们也属于我的工作范畴。我常常鼓励学生们进行设计，并作为顾问参与开发过程，审批最终的设计结果。

From 1981 until my emeritus status in 1997, I taught at the Hamburg University of Fine Arts alongside my job as head of the design department at Braun. I viewed my work in Hamburg as both an opportunity and a duty. Good design begins with the education of good designers.

I find the quality of design teaching in Germany to be questionable to say the least. The main reason for this is the abundance of colleges. Most of them are not able to educate industrial designers to meet the high level of complex requirements needed in practice today and for the future. The works of my students, a few of which I would like to show here, are not my designs, just as the many products designed by my team at Braun are not mine either. They belong nevertheless within the context of my work. I often nudged the designs along, accompanied their development as an advisor, and approved the final results.

 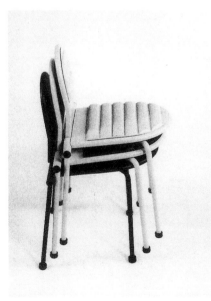 

该主题所示图片为1981—1993年设计专业学生的作品
上图: 椅子设计 [安吉拉·诺普 (Angela Knoop)]

Images on the following pages show works by design students between 1981 and 1993
Above: Chair design (Angela Knoop)

例如，美术学院礼堂的椅子设计方案就是通过在学生内部举行竞赛产生的。这款椅子可以根据需要堆叠起来，也可以排成一行。这里最重要的设计要求就是椅子要能够由汉堡的手工业公司制作出来，因此就生产难度而言，它的结构是非常简单的，只需把钢管进行弯折就可以了。

The design of a chair for the auditorium of the University of Fine Arts, for example, came out of an internal competition. As the assignment required, it can be stacked and arranged in rows. The most important requirement was that the chair be capable of being manufactured by Hamburg handcraft companies. In terms of technical production, the construction is therefore very simple: bent steel tubing.

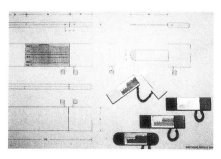 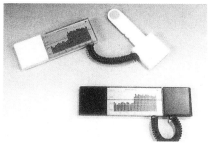

为安全期避孕所设计的温度计，液晶显示屏上显示了一个月内的体温读数（安吉拉·诺普）

Design for a thermometer for the Knaus-Ogino contraception method. A LCD display shows the temperatures taken during the course of one month (Angela Knoop)

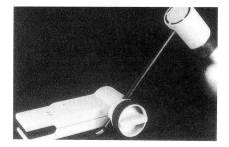  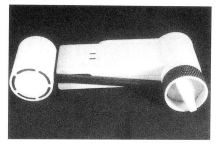

图夹式台灯设计（安吉拉·诺普）

Photo clamping lamp design (Angela Knoop)

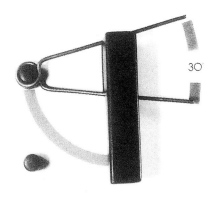

图夹式台灯的设计基础来自对夹具力学的研究。设计师开发出一种借助杠杆非常容易打开的夹具，并通过制作功能模型对其进行探索和优化。

卤素桌面台灯（第118页）的设计概念是在桌子下面用一根导轨对台灯进行可调节的固定。因此，台灯可以在水平方向上来回移动。

The basis for the design of the clamping lamp came from investigations into the mechanics of clamps. The solution – a clamp that was very easy to open, thanks to a lever – was explored and optimised by making functional models.

The conceptual idea behind the halogen desk lamp (p. 118) is the variable attachment, which uses a track at the back of the table. This allows the lamp to be moved around horizontally.

图夹式台灯的功能模型
Photo clamping lamp – functional model

卤素桌面台灯的设计[安德烈亚斯·哈克巴特 (Andreas Hackbarth)]
Design for a halogen desk lamp (Andreas Hackbarth)

　　在保温杯（第119页）的设计案例中，设计师使用有2个圆筒的瓶身代替通常情况下只有1个圆筒的瓶身。这个创意是令人惊讶的，同时也是令人信服的。尽管它的容量只有1升，但是双筒瓶身看起来更紧凑、更容易固定，也更便于运输。这款保温杯可以用背带挂在肩膀上，也可以直接用手拎着。

　　固定在保温杯顶部的2个容器是非常实用的小配件，它们可以用来装牛奶、糖或柠檬等。

The thermos flask (p. 119) both surprised and convinced with the idea of making the body out of two cylinders instead of one, as is normally the case. The double cylinder appears compact despite its one litre capacity and is much easier to hold. It is also easier to transport. The bottle can be attached to a carrying strap and thus hung over the shoulder or, by using the strap as a handle, carried in the hand.

One of its most sensible improvements is the two-chambered container that can be affixed to the top and can hold extras such as milk, sugar or lemon.

这款投币式自助洗衣机的设计核心是关于整个洗涤过程的生态设计。在这里，洗涤过程应该消耗尽可能少的能源、清洁剂和水。

电脑控制的洗衣称重秤可以使洗衣机为每位顾客提供最佳的洗涤、烘干和熨烫程序。电脑的计算结果会存储在磁卡上，这样通过磁卡就可以控制时间、温度、洗涤剂的量及水量。这套洗衣设施有一个封闭的水循环系统，可以循环往复地清洗和备水。洗衣机及其所有系统部件都是以简

The ecological design of the entire washing process is central to this design of a launderette. Here, washing should consume as little energy, detergent and water as possible.

A computer-controlled scale for weighing the laundry calculates the optimal programme for washing, drying and ironing for each customer. This calculation is then stored on a magnetic card, which controls time, temperature, detergent dose or water quantity. The laundry facility has a closed water system that cleans and prepares the water again

保温杯的设计［玛雅·戈杰斯（ Maja Gorges ）］　*Design of a thermos flask (Maja Gorges)*

带称重终端和水循环系统的自助洗衣机［彼得·埃卡德（ Peter Eckard ），乔亨·亨克尔斯（ Jochen Henkels ）］
Design of a launderette with weighing terminal and water recycling system (Peter Eckard, Jochen Henkels)

单、功能性和模块化的方式进行设计的，因此它们可以相互组合并构造出不同尺寸和配置的自助洗衣房。

本页下图所示的设计案例是一辆电动自行车。该设计的目的是通过增加驱动力、改进行李搬运能力、提供有效的防雨保护等设计细节对自行车进行改良，以大幅提升普通自行车的内在价值。具体的设计方案：在自行车的前轮上有一个电动辅助驱动装置，车身框架采用碳纤维材质，车身的集成式行李架带有一个大而稳定、向后延伸的行李架，此外还有一个大的折叠式雨披装在车把之中。

and again. The washing machines, along with all of the other system components, are designed in a simple, functional and modular way, allowing for the construction of launderettes of varying sizes and configurations.

The design on page 120 shows an electric bicycle. The aim here was to significantly upgrade the intrinsic value of an ordinary bicycle by augmenting the drive, improving luggage carrying and providing effective rain protection. The bike has an electrically powered auxiliary drive in the front wheel. The frame is carbon fibre. The integrated luggage holder is extended with a large, stable luggage rack and a large foldout rain cape is stowed compactly in the handlebar.

右图：带有称重秤和付款装置的洗衣房（第119页）终端设计（详图）
Right: Design for the laundry terminal (page 119) with scales and pay unit (detail)

电动自行车的设计［马蒂亚斯·塞勒（Mathias Seiler），格德·施米塔（Gerd Schmieta），希尔玛·耶迪克（Hilmar Jaedicke）］
Electric bicycle design (Mathias Seiler, Gerd Schmieta, Hilmar Jaedicke)

本页下面2图、第122页上面2图所示图片展示了一款可移动、可折叠的轻便童车的设计方案。它在车轴框架之间设有一个很大的收纳箱，这是一个非常实用的改良设计，收纳箱内的物品可以用网罩固定。这个收纳箱可以随着小车一起折叠并再次打开，因此无须重新安装。小车的折叠过程特别简单，用一只手（或一只脚）将收纳箱拉到座椅下面即可。小车折叠起来后就可以像手推车一样四处移动，这个便利性设计对有爬楼梯或搭乘公共交通工具的人而言是非常重要的。小车的横向尺寸为58厘米，因此很容易通过公共汽车和火车的车门。小车的座椅部分被刻意抬高，以便使小车上的婴儿座位可以保持在汽车排气管的位置以上。

Images on pages 121 and 122 show a design for a light, mobile, foldable child's buggy. It has a large luggage box between the axles, which is a very sensible improvement. Its contents can be secured with a net – the buggy can then be folded and opened again without having to unload it first. The folding procedure is particularly simple – you pull the luggage box with one hand (or a foot) up under the seat. Once folded, the buggy can then be moved around like a sack barrow, which is important for dealing with stairs or getting into public transport. With an axial dimension of 58 centimetres it fits easily through bus and train doors. The seat is elevated so that the child stays above car exhaust pipe level.

童车的设计 [科西玛·斯特里佩（ Cosima Striepe）]
Design for a baby buggy (Cosima Striepe)

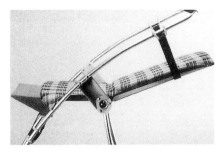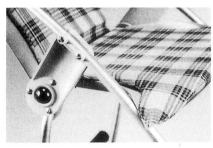

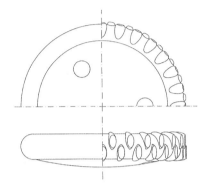

改善公共交通状况的方法之一是设计出更好的公交站，使它们能提供更多的舒适性、信息和安全性。本页和第122页的设计方案提出了一个新颖的模块化公交系统，可以用来构建各种规模和类型的公交站。在该公交系统中，公交站的墙体选用了玻璃和钢材来制作，这主要是基于安全方面的考虑，因为可视性非常重要。公交站顶棚选用了铝和塑料材质，而其他所有必要的部件，如折叠式座椅、站立辅助设备、电话、紧急按钮、售票机和交互式信息终端等均安装在一根水平的铝管上面。公交站还与一台中央总控计算机相连，这台计算机能够通知乘客当前的交通状况或为乘客提供出行指导。

One of the many ways to improve public transport is to design better bus stops. They should offer more comfort, information and safety. The design on page 121–122 envisages a new modular system for bus stops of various sizes and constellations. Made of steel profiles and glass, the walls provide visibility, which is important for safety. The roof is of aluminium and plastic. All the necessary components, such as folding seats, supports, telephone, emergency button, ticket machine and an interactive information terminal are mounted on a continuous, horizontal aluminium profile. The bus stop is connected to a central computer that informs travellers about the current traffic situation or provides travel directions.

公共汽车站/火车站设计（比约恩·克林）
Design for a bus/train stop for public transport (Björn Kling)

公共交通的交互式信息终端和折叠椅的设计
（比约恩·克林）

*Design for an interactive information terminal
and folding chairs for public transport (Björn
Kling)*

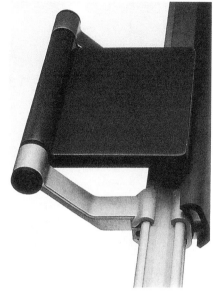

本页显示的是运动自行车的一个设计模型。它带有一个大的、飞速旋转的中心车轮，从这一点可以看出它的功能由设计直接清晰地传达了出来。自行车的操控部件位于车身顶部，并通过不同的形式和颜色加以强调。用户可以在无须借用任何额外工具的情况下，根据坐姿与训练要求调整自行车的座位和把手。

The design of an exercise bicycle (page 123) shows a model whose function is indicated by its design – you can see the large central flywheel turning. The electro-mechanical unit sits above, accentuated through form and colour. The saddle and handlebars can be adjusted from the sitting position to fit users and their training position exactly, without any additional tools.

运动自行车的设计（比约恩·克林）
Design for an exercise bike (Björn Kling)

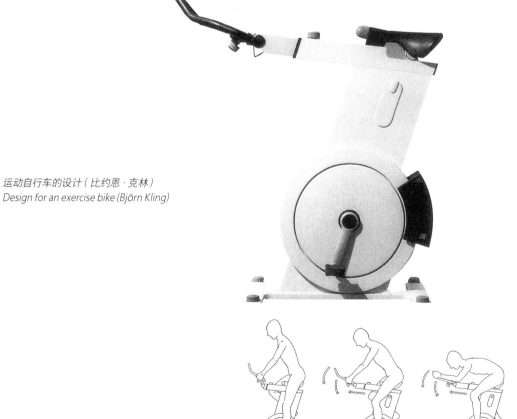

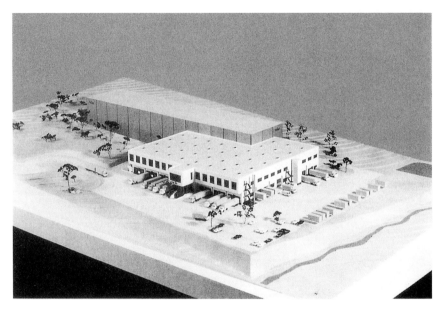

位于阿尔特菲尔德（*Altfeld*）的博朗配送中心（*1994年*）
Braun distribution centre in Altfeld (1994)

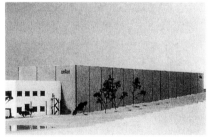

　　博朗的设计团队也全面参与了公司建筑物的设计。我们就建筑物的总体设计和内部空间设计提出相关的建议和具体方案，同时也提供支持。我们的任务之一就是要确保建筑物的外观与公司的内在精神保持一致性，也就是要符合企业形象。

　　其中一个很好的案例就是1994年投入运营的位于阿尔特菲尔德的博朗配送中心。设计这座现代配送中心大楼的主要挑战来自技术方面。该中心大楼包括一个大型储藏库、一个拣货区及货物进出区。在

The design team at Braun was fully involved in of the design the company's buildings as well. It advised, supported and made concrete proposals for the overall design and the interior areas. It was part of our mandate to concern ourselves with a comprehensive appearance that reflected the company's spirit – in short to pay attention to what is now called Corporate Design.

The Braun distribution centre in Altfeld, which came into operation in 1994, is a good example. The design of modern distribution centre is primarily a technical challenge. The centre

博朗设计团队的支持下，这个建筑项目的主要任务是设计出能够与周围景观融为一体的巨大建筑体量，同时还要传达出博朗品牌的独特标准。

最后，大型储藏库被设计在一个斜坡上，并使其尽可能地沉入地下。它的外墙立面呈现出一种淡淡的哑光金属灰色，从而与天空的浅蓝色及灰色相得益彰，而位于储藏库前面较平坦的低层建筑的外墙立面则采用了与其颜色对比鲜明的白色。

另一个我们参与设计的建筑案例是位于克伦伯格的博朗行政大楼，它于1979年完工。这座大楼有着深灰色的外墙立面，与10年前建成的博朗总部大楼建筑群交相辉映。这座结构复杂的建筑看上去既稳定又自成一体。

combines a large storage facility, a consignment area and the entrance and exit areas for goods. The main architectural task, supported by the Braun design team, was to design the vast building volume in such a way as to integrate well into the landscape, but at the same time to communicate the special standards of the Braun brand.

The storage facility was recessed into the ground as far as possible on the sloping site. The facade is a light, matt, metallic grey that harmonises well with the blues and greys of the sky. The flatter, low-rise distribution centre set in front is a contrasting white colour.

The administration building in Kronberg, completed in 1979, has a dark grey facade, which complements the Braun headquarters building complex built ten years previously. The building has a sophisticated structure and appears both calm and self-contained.

位于克伦伯格（Kronberg）的博朗行政大楼（1979年）

Braun administration building in Kronberg (1979)

FSB公司的项目

1985年，业内领先的配件制造商FSB（Franz Schneider Brakel）公司邀请来自世界各地的著名设计师参加其举办的比赛。设计师们的参赛作品于1986年秋季在一个研讨会上展出，主要有门把手、球形把手和门窗拉手等产品。FSB公司将其中一些设计作品投入生产，其中也包括了我设计的2款门把手。我的目标是设计出尽可能简单的把手。要知道，我们今天的生活环境非常复杂多样，我一直致力消除这种混乱性。

FSB corporation

In 1985 a leading fittings manufacturer FSB, Franz Schneider Brakel, invited a group of renowned designers from all over the world to a competition. The resulting fitting designs –primarily door handles, knobs and pulls –were then shown at a workshop in autumn 1986. FSB put some of the designs into production, including two door handles that I designed. My aim was to design handles that were as simple as possible. Our living environment today is complex and polymorphic enough. I have always striven to counteract this chaos.

在洛蒂斯（Rotis）向奥托·艾舍展示
参赛作品
Presentation the results of the FSB
competition to Otl Aicher in Rotis

尽管这2款门把手看上去形式简单，但它们都可以通过略微弯曲的侧面细节设计而被轻松抓握。rgs 2系列门把手的设计是由我和我的学生安吉拉·诺普合作完成的。然后，我们又进一步开发了rgs 2型号的基本形状，并由此产生了rgs 3门把手。至今，我依然认为这2款门把手是关于"抓与握"设计的优秀案例。

rgs 2、rgs 3产品与rgs 1产品一样，其零部件和外表面都是由铸铝材质制成的，抓握部位则是由热塑性塑料制成的。热塑性塑料还凸显了这款产品的独有特点：门把手上的食指凹槽弧线在一定程度上延展了手柄的抓握长度。rgs 3门把手作为变形设计，则是在面向大门的门把手内侧部分将食指凹槽演化为了一个小指凹槽。

两种不同材料的组合设计特色鲜明：一方面，金属材质在视觉上提供了高科技的酷感；另一方面，热塑性塑料材质又使手易于抓握。

Despite their simplicity, both door handles are easy to grip, thanks to their lightly curved sides. The rgs 2 series design is based on a collaboration between myself and one of my students at the time, Angela Knoop. Then I developed basic shape of the rgs 2 model further in detail until the rgs 3 variations emerged. I think both handles are still good examples for the idea of 'grab and grip'.

As with rgs 1, the structural parts as well as the face of the models rgs 2/ rgs 3 are made of cast aluminium; the grip areas are made of thermoplastic. This reveals the special quality of the design: an indentation for the index finger on the neck of the handle extends the grip. With the variation where the return faces the door (rgs 3), the index finger indentation mutates into an indentation for the little finger.

The two different materials also offer technically cool metal for the eye and grip-friendly thermoplastic for the hand.

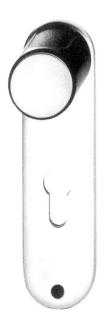

家具
Furniture

我大约在60年前开始设计家具，在这个过程中，我逐渐开发出很多适用范围广泛的多功能家具。这些家具产品最初是由维瑟与扎普夫（Vitsoe & Zapf）公司生产的，后来改由威斯·维瑟（Wiese Vitsoe）公司和sdr+公司生产，现在则是由维瑟公司生产。

I started designing furniture systems some 60 years ago. Over time a broad and versatile programme has developed. It was produced initially by Vitsoe & Zapf, then Wiese Vitsoe, sdr+ and now by Vitsoe.

我设计的许多家具产品在市场上都销售了很长时间，其中的一些设计作品还成为广为人知的产品，如606通用货架。

在我回顾这个重要的设计阶段前，我想先说一说自己在设计家具时的出发点和考量因素。我设计的家具产品也许比博朗的产品能更直接地反映我关于世界应该如何"装饰"及人们应该如何在这种人造环境中生活的想法。从这个意义上来说，我所设计的每一件家具都是为这个世界而设

Many of the products were on the market for a long time. Some of the designs, such as the 606 shelving system, are well-known.

A version of this system made completely from aluminium is produced by De Padua in Milan.

In looking back on this very important segment of my design work I would like to attempt to explain my motives and considerations whilst designing furniture. My furniture reflects, perhaps even more directly than the Braun

620休闲椅方案（1962年）："这款扶手椅的设计是具有高度美学价值的、个性化的原创。"正是基于这个理由，它在1973年10月10日的法院判决中取得了设计专利保护
620 Lounge chair programm (1962): 'The design of this chair is a personal, original creation of a highly aesthetic value.' This was the court's justification in patenting the design on 10th Oct. 1973

计的，都是为了表达该如何在这个世界中生活而设计的：它们体现了我对人类的基本看法。

20世纪50年代，我持有的是历经了独裁、战争和毁灭冲击后的年轻人所持有的信念。同时，我也在百废待兴的前几年体验到了同样强烈的自由。

products, the results of my ideas about how the world should be ' furnished ' and how people could best live in this artificial environment. In this respect, every piece of my furniture is a design for the world and how to live in it. It reflects a view of mankind as I see it.

In the 1950s my beliefs were those of a young man who had experienced dictatorship, war and destruction as intensively as I had experienced the freedom of the first years of an optimistic new beginning.

简而言之，在我以建筑师的身份接受教育培训和工作期间，我熟悉了一种新的装饰世界的设计方法。它们给我留下了深刻印象，并反过来激励我去做自己的设计。我正处在那样一个人生阶段，即对于一个人应该如何生活及应该在什么样的环境中生活有了自己的想法。

对我来说，我设计的家具所具备的最重要的品质是什么呢？

我认为是它们的简单与克制。对于一个摆满了书的书架而言，书架本身应该是几乎看不见的。我设计的所有家具都是以这样一种态度设计出来的，我曾经用一句看似自相矛盾的话来表达我的理念：好的

To put it succinctly: during my training and work as an architect I became acquainted with designs for a new way of furnishing the world. They impressed me, and in turn motivated me to make my own designs. I was also in that phase of life in which one develops one's own ideas about how, and in what kind of environment one wants to live.

What was for me back then, and indeed today, the most important quality to be found in the furniture systems I designed?

I think it is their simplicity, their reserve. A bookcase system full of books becomes, itself, almost invisible. All the furniture pieces are designed from an attitude that I once expressed in the somewhat paradoxical

622椅子方案（1962年），适用于办公室、候诊室、演讲厅等
622 Chair programme (1962) for the office, the waiting room, the lecture theatre ...

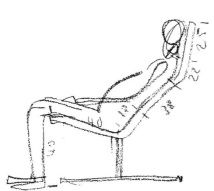

设计就是尽可能少的设计（Good design is as little design as possible）。减少设计的目的绝不是我和其他志同道合的设计师所被指责的那样——为了制造毫无意义的稀疏。恰恰相反，它意味着从被"事物"支配的地位中解放出来的自由。我想为自己设计一种生活环境，创造出一个可以由自

statement: Good design is as little design as possible. The aim of design reduction is by no means the sterile sparseness that I and other like-minded designers have been accused of producing. Instead it is the freedom from the dominance of ' things'. I wanted to design and have for myself a living environment that created free space that one could configure

601/602椅子方案（1960年）
601/602 chair programme (1960)

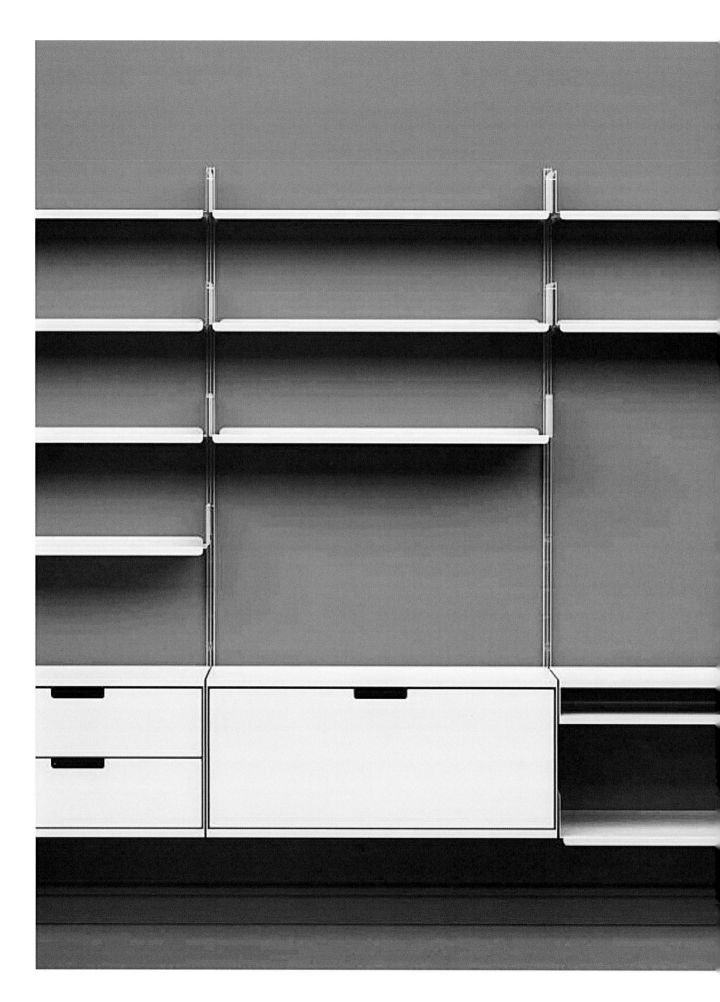

己支配的自由空间、一个可以灵活移动的空间、一个允许改变的空间。我发现，不论是在过去还是现在，具有典型代表性或风格鲜明的居家环境对于生活在其中的人具有一种局限性和压迫性。从某种程度上而言，围绕在我们周围的众多人工制品具有某种破坏性。

我曾经说过，我的目标是减省一切多余的东西，以便为必要的东西腾出地方。从这一点出发去展开设计工作所产生的效果将是平静、愉快、易于理解和持久的。我所设计的家具的持久生命力是令人信服的。这些货架、桌子和椅子的简单性超越了任何一种会过时的设计，因为它们从不追随任何时尚潮流。

totally individually, a space for movement and one that permitted change. I found, and still find, representative or emphatically homely environments to be limiting and oppressive. The overwhelming variety and shapes and sizes of the artefacts that surround us have something destructive about them.

I once said that my aim is to leave out everything superfluous in order to allow the essential to come through. The resulting forms will be calm, pleasant, understandable and long-lived. The durability of my furniture designs has become convincingly clear. In their simplicity, the cupboards, tables and chairs are beyond any kind of design that can age because it does not submit to the zeitgeist.

搭配620椅子方案的边桌（1963年）
Side table for chair programme 620 (1963)

570桌子方案和571/572模块化家具组装系统（1957年）
Table programme 570 and montage system 571/72 (1957)

620休息椅方案（1962年）和606通用置物架系统（1960年）
Lounge chair programme 620 (1962) and universal shelving system 606 (1960)

对我来说，家具的第2个重要品质是实用性（具体包含了很多方面）。扶手椅和椅子应该便于人们自由、放松、舒适地坐着。它们应该易于保养，能够符合使用者的意愿，并在需求发生变化时能够相应做出改变。这就意味着家具在功能上必须具有一定的中立性。也就是说，这些产品应该适用于各种不同的场景，而不是仅适用于客厅、卧室、餐厅或办公室。

我设计的大部分家具都是以模块系统的形式呈现出来的。这些具有模块单元的产品系统允许用户对其进行各种可能的变化布置。置物架、桌子和墙板也是体现这一设计特点的典型例子。但即便是看起

The second quality important to me, with all my furniture, is of course its usability – in many dimensions. The armchairs and chairs should facilitate unfettered, relaxed and comfortable sitting. They should be easy to maintain. They should be adaptable to their owners' wishes and changeable when requirements change. In this respect it is vital that this furniture has a degree of functional neutrality. That means the pieces should work in a variety of different situations, not just specifically for the living room, bedroom, dining room or the office.

Most of my furniture has been designed in the form of systems. Systems with modular elements allow a variety of possible variable

610衣柜/壁板系统（1961年）：利用这个产品，用户可以在厨房或浴室中安排衣橱及多功能区
610 Wardrobe/wall panel system (1961): With this programme you can build wardrobes as well as versatile, functional areas in the kitchen or bathroom

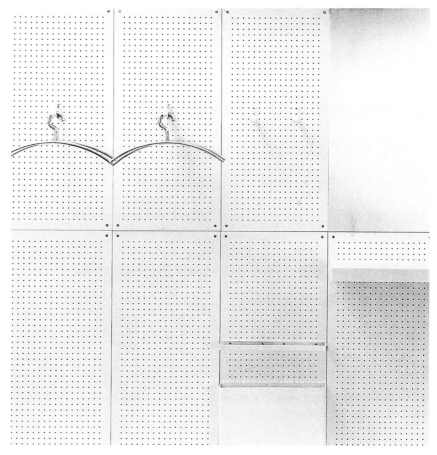

配置了570模块化组装系统（1957年）的卧室
Bedroom furnished with the 570 montage system (1957)

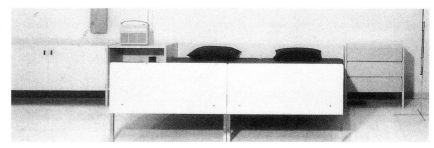

850会议桌方案（1985年）：这款850会议桌为用户的腿部提供了舒适的空间。这要归功于居中安装的管状钢支腿，这些支腿里面还填充了钢制车床废料，从而提高了支腿的稳定性
Conference table programme 850 (1985): The 850 conference table programme offered good legroom thanks to centrally-placed, tubular steel legs, which were weighted with steel lathe for greater stability

862会议椅（1986年）：与于尔根·格雷贝尔联合设计
Conference chair 862 (1986) designed with Jürgen Greubel

来独立的产品，如620扶手椅，其实也是从系统的角度进行设计的。它的所有部件（如扶手或靠背）均采用了模块化设计。这些椅子很容易拆卸、拼接或互换。例如，用户可以毫不费力地将一把扶手椅改装成一张能坐两三人甚至更多人的沙发。

这种在设计中对可用性、可变性和耐用性的追求，要求产品必须具有非常高的质量水平。维瑟家具系统应该且可以经受数10年的使用、扩展、形式转换和移动而不会出现损坏。

set-ups. The shelving system, the table programme and the wall panel system are particularly good examples of this. But even the apparently solitary products, such as the 620 armchair, are systems as well. All the components such as the arm or backrests are designed in a modular way. They are easy to detach, connect, or exchange. An armchair, for example, can be converted without much effort into a sofa seating two, three or even more people.

My endeavours to achieve usability, variety and durability require very high levels of quality. A Vitsoe furniture system should be able to withstand decades of use, extension, alteration and moving without harm – and it can.

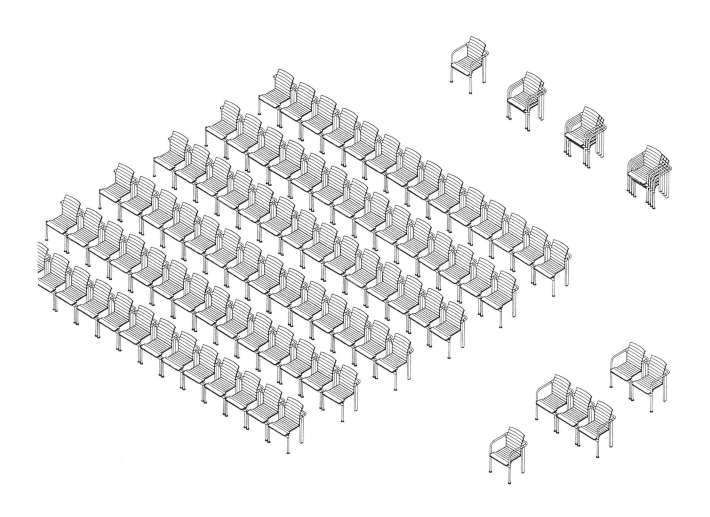

这种对于高质量产品的追求导致产品价格上涨，从而使得这些看似简单、经济实用的家具形成了某种无意义的排他性。

在家具设计方面，我试图实现一种既不具有代表性，也不具有装饰性的审美品质，它并不想给人留下深刻印象，而是成为产品功能性的一部分。这种审美品质的实现来自结构的清晰和透明，来自尺寸和比例的平衡，来自对材料表面的精心处理，尤其是考虑到了每个产品系统的最微小的细节——每个螺丝钉。对我来说，生活环境或单个物体的审美品质是植根于和谐所形成的平静，而不是某个独特的形状或颜色带来的刺激。

This high quality has led to prices that have lent these apparently simple, uncomplicated, materially economical, functional furniture objects a degree of exclusivity that was never intended.

With the furniture designs, I tried to achieve an aesthetic quality that is neither representative nor decorative, that doesn't try to impress, but is a part of its own utility. This quality comes from a clarity and transparency of disposition, through the balance of size and proportions, through the painstaking treatment of the surfaces, and not least because each system is thought through to the tiniest detail – literally each and every screw. For me personally, the aesthetic quality of a living environment or a single object is rooted in a calm that comes from harmony, not in the stimuli of pronounced forms and colours.

我的家

我在克伦伯格的房子毗邻陶努斯（Taunus）林地，是我早期帮助博朗规划的集中住宅开发项目的一部分。这栋房子是按照我自己的设计方案建造和装修的，我和妻子（摄影师）从1971年起就住在这里。毫无疑问，我们是用维瑟家具来布置居家环境的。这样做有两个原因：一是因为我只设计自己想要的家具，二是通过日常使用来深入了解这些家具可以让我更好地认识到它们还有哪些地方可以改进。对于一些我需要而维瑟公司还未开发的家具，我会从其他制造商那里选购以类似角度设计的家具，如我们用于搭配维瑟720桌子的弯曲木托耐特（Thonet）214号椅子，以及摆放在厨房和生活区之间的早餐区域内的弗里茨·汉森（Fritz Hansen）凳子。

My Home

My house in Kronberg, bordering the Taunus woodlands, is part of a concentrated housing development that I had originally helped to plan. The house is built and furnished according to my own design and I have lived here with my photographer wife since 1971. It goes without saying that we live with Vitsoe furniture systems; first, because I have only ever designed furniture that I myself would like to have, and second, getting to know the systems in daily use allows me to better recognise where they might be improved or developed further. In instances where the Vitsoe programme is not complete, I have selected furniture from other manufacturers that have been designed from a similar perspective, such as the bent wood 214 Thonet chairs around the Vitsoe 720 table that we use for dining, or the Fritz Hansen stools at the breakfast bar between the kitchen and living area.

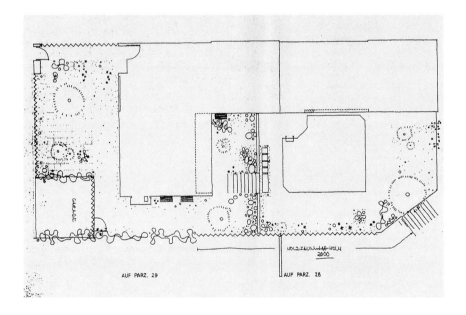

生活区

Living Area

房子中起居室的中心区摆放着一组620扶手椅，这里是我的景观位，从这儿我可以看到生机勃勃的花园。此外，这里还是有着多种功能用途的区域。

在这里，我们可以围坐在一起聊天、招待朋友、看电视。我们在室内摆放了植物、书籍和画作以营造环境氛围。这些房间的装饰布置体现了我的设计背后所包含的基本意图：简单、本质和开放。这些物品既不夸张，也不会占据中心舞台或限制住户的活动，而是悄悄地退居幕后。它们

In the centre of the living room area there is a loose group of 620 armchairs, my version of a seating landscape. It is a lively and much-used area with a view of the garden.

Here is where we sit together, talk, entertain our friends and watch television. Plants, books and pictures lend atmosphere. The composition of these rooms represents the basic intention behind my design: simplicity, essentiality and openness. The objects do not boast about themselves, take centre stage or restrict, but withdraw into the background.

的克制和低调提供了空间感。秩序性对于人类并不是一种限制，而是一种解放。生活在一个令人不安的空间环境里形成的是破坏性的喧闹和视觉混乱。在我看来，设计的任务是保持安静，创造出让人们回归自我的平静。与此相反的则是那种极具刺激性的设计，它想要吸引人们的注意力并激发人们强烈的情感。对我来说，这是不符合人性的，因为它增加了混乱，使我们困惑、麻木和裹足不前。

Their reduction and unobtrusiveness generate space. The orderliness is not restrictive but liberating. In a world which is filling up at a disconcerting pace, that is destructively loud and visually confusing, design has the task in my view to be quiet, to help generate a level of calm that allows people to return to themselves. The contrary position is a design that strongly stimulates, that wants to draw attention to itself and arouse strong emotions. For me this is inhumane because it adds in its way to the chaos that confuses, numbs and lames us.

工作区

此外，我在自己的房子里可以像在博朗的办公室里一样，通过这些产品来调整自己的感官和敏感度。我经常在家工作，待在一个像客厅一样的通向花园的房间里。我的工作与通常意义上的设计不同，更多的是沉思、阅读和交谈。设计首先是一个思维过程。

日本传统建筑的房间设计与我的室内设计理念很相似：在空旷的房间中，地板、墙壁和天花板有着清晰而精确的布局，材料和结构也是精心组合的。这种美学要比欧洲富丽堂皇的、图案化的和喧闹的美学更精妙。

Working area

Inside my house, just like in my office at Braun, I can adjust my senses and my sensitivity. I often work at home – in a room that opens out on to the garden, just like the living room. Working for me does not mean so much designing in the usual sense of the term, but more contemplation, reading and talking. Design is in the first instance a thinking process.

In traditional Japanese architecture, living spaces are designed from a position that is similar to my own. The aesthetic of an empty room with its clear and precise organisation of floor, walls and ceiling and careful combination of materials and structure is much more sophisticated then the European aesthetic of opulence, pattern and loud forms.

我在设计自己的小花园时也深受日本花园设计的启发。这个小花园并不是复制任何特定的日本花园，而是对日本花园精神的致敬，并将其转化为适用于我们的时代、景观和气候的一种阐述。

我觉得在花园里工作会让人着迷，这也是一种设计工作，甚至可以与设计房间、家具或电器的工作相媲美。花园里的

In the design of my relatively small garden, I have allowed myself to be inspired by Japanese gardens. It is not a copy of any specific garden, rather a homage to the essence of the Japanese garden, a translation into our time, our landscape and our climate.

I find working in the garden stimulating – it is a kind of design work that is comparable with designing a room, a furniture system or an

从内到外，从外到内

From within to without, from without to within

小游泳池是令人愉快的，但它不是奢侈品，而是我进行治疗的必需品。

听起来可能令人难以置信，我作为20世纪末技术产品的设计师，也会从日本传统建筑设计文化中汲取灵感，并以完全尊重和认可的态度看待其成就。但是，如果在漫长的设计历程中没有任何东西能够激发我或帮助我坚定信念，那就更令人难以置信了。在我看来，许多当代设计师的一个不足就是对历史缺乏兴趣。

appliance. The small swimming pool in the garden is delightful but no luxury, rather a therapeutic necessity for me.

It may seem surprising that I, as a designer of the late twentieth century, as a designer of technical products, also draw inspiration from design cultures such as traditional Japanese architecture and view their achievements with total respect and recognition. But it would be even more surprising if there were nothing in the long history of design that had inspired me or helped strengthen my beliefs. The lack of historic interest in many contemporary designers is, in my view, a weakness.

就像古老的日本设计文化一样，我同样也被浪漫主义时期的建筑所吸引。中世纪莱茵高（Rheingau）地区的埃伯巴赫（Eberbach）修道院是罗马式建筑明珠之一，它离我的家乡威斯巴登不远。我年轻时经常去那里参观。在我看来，另一个杰出的建筑是位于意大利阿普利亚（Apulia）的建于13世纪的八角形蒙特城堡（Castel del Monte），它是由霍亨斯陶芬（Hohenstaufen）王朝的腓特烈二世（Frederick II）建造的。

多年前我便对夏克风格（Shaker style）熟稔于心。它那直截了当的设计、完美的持久性及对优秀设计解决方案的尊重，都令我印象深刻。

Just as with the old Japanese design culture, I feel equally drawn to the architecture of the romantic period. The medieval Eberbach Monastery in Rheingau is one of the pearls of Romanesque architecture and lies not far from my native city of Wiesbaden. I visited it often when I was young. Another most exceptional architectural achievement is, in my mind, the octagonal thirteenth-century Castel del Monte in Apulia, Italy, built by the emperor Frederick II of Hohenstaufen.

Years ago I became acquainted with Shaker design, which deeply impressed me with its straightforward approach, its patient perfection and respectful regard for good solutions.

在第46届国际设计师大会上做的演讲原文，美国科罗拉多州阿斯彭市（Aspen）（1993年）
Lecture given at the 46th International Designer Congress, Aspen, Colorado/USA (1993)

设计的未来

未来的设计将是什么样？应当根据哪些目标、要求和标准设计产品？设计的意义和价值又是什么呢？

我们迫切需要一种对设计的反思，这种反思能够感知并认真对待未来的现实，但这种反思才刚刚开始。

人类的工业技术文明正威胁着地球上生命的生存，因此，一场影响深远的变革是不可避免的。但或许这场变革我们可以有意识地去进行，而不是被灾难逼迫着去进行。也许通过这场变革，我们可以让生活不至于变得越来越贫困，而是变得更富有人性。

产品文化危机迫使我们去采用新的设计伦理：在未来，设计的价值必须通过其对整个人类生存的贡献来判断。

这一贡献具有重要意义。一方面，设计可以为产品的直接原材料和生态质量的持续改进提供动力。另一方面，更重要的是产品的设计还有助于促进整个产品数量的持续减少。因此，未来几十年的产品文化目标将是"少，但更好"。

如今，"购买刺激"美学几乎完全支配了设计的方式，并助长了破坏性产品的生产和浪费，它必须让位于支持产品长期经济耐用的美学。

然而，改变产品文化并不能依靠洞察力、善意和理性诉求等来实现。如果可以的话，它只能通过人类行为的改变和消费结构的改变来实现。

The Future of Design

What will design be in the coming years? According to which goals, requirements and criteria will products be designed? Where will the importance and the values of design lie?

A reflection upon design that perceives and takes the realities of tomorrow seriously is sorely needed, yet has hardly begun.

Our technical-industrial civilisation is threatening to destroy the potential for continued life on earth. Far-reaching change is unavoidable. But perhaps there is a chance for this change to be consciously executed rather than forced upon us by catastrophe. And perhaps there's a chance that this change will not lead to an impoverishment of our lives, but will make them richer in a humane sense.

The crisis in our product culture is forcing us to adopt a new design ethic: in the future, the value of design must be judged by its contribution to overall survival.

This contribution is of great importance. Design is capable of providing an impulse towards constant improvements in the immediate material and ecological qualities of a product. And, much more importantly, the design of products has a duty to contribute to a sustainable reduction in the number of products as a whole. Therefore the goal for product culture in the coming decades will be "less, but better".

The 'purchase stimulation' aesthetic that almost completely governs design today, whereby it becomes the fuel for destructive product waste, has to give way to an aesthetic that supports the conservative long-term use of products.

However, a changed product culture will not be achieved by insight, goodwill and appeals for rationality. Changes in behaviour can – if at all – only be effected through structural change.

例如，开发出一个消费品的闭环系统。在这个系统中，产品依然为制造商所有，用户不必为拥有它们而付费，而是为了使用它们提供的服务而付费。用户用完之后，产品会返回到制造商那里进行翻新和维修，然后再返还给用户或制造商直接对产品进行回收利用。

这种消费结构的变化将有可能改变人们的行为，并因此而改变设计的方向。在这种情况下，设计的主要目标将不再是刺激消费者去购买，而是增加产品的长期使用价值。

设计师、设计机构和设计公司的职责是找到消费结构变化的起点，然后思考、启动、实施计划，并向人们展示这种新的方式。

可以说，设计塑造了我们生活中的事物和生活环境，它具有重要的决定性意义。40年前，当我还是一名年轻设计师时就对这一点深信不疑。今天，我更是深信不疑。

当前，致力优秀设计的设计师和设计公司面临着一项艰巨任务：改变我们的世界，让世界变得更好。换句话说，就是对那些丑陋的、不人道的、令人恼火的、破坏性的、资源耗竭的、压抑的和困惑的所有方面进行更好的设计。显然，我们在这里谈论的主题所涵盖的范围很广，从日常用品一直到城市的整体形态。

在人造产品中，有太多东西是丑陋的、低效的、令人沮丧及混乱的。

最近，我读到了几句深深触动我的话。不同寻常的是它们竟然出自一本漫画书：

"菲比俯视着这些坐落在洛杉矶平缓山丘和山谷中的粉红色房屋，她陷入了对生活的思考：这一切都意味着什么呢？"

毫无疑问，如果有人从外面看我们这个世界，看到我们对它所做的一切，也会问自己同样关于人类和生命的问题："这一切都意味着什么呢？"

One example is the development of closed systems for consumer goods. In these systems the products remain the property of the manufacturers. You don't pay to own them, but to use them and for servicing. After use, the products go back to their producers to be updated, repaired and sent back to their users, or to be recycled.

This structure would enable a behavioural change, and thereby a change in design. The main design goal here would not be to stimulate the consumer to buy, but, rather, optimal long-term use value.

Designers, design institutions and companies have a duty to find starting points for structural changes such as this, to think through, to carry out, to start experimental projects and to demonstrate new paths.

Design, the shaping of things that we live with and the shaping of our environment, is of decisive importance. I was convinced of that 40 years ago as a young, unknown designer, and I am even more convinced of it today.

The designers and companies who strive towards good design have a big task ahead of them: To transform our world – to better design all the aspects that are ugly, inhuman, irritating, destructive, draining, oppressive and confusing. You know as well as I do the huge scope of what we are talking about here –from the smallest everyday objects right up to the shape of our cities.

Far too much of what is man-made is ugly, inefficient, depressing chaos.

Recently I came across a couple of sentences that greatly affected me – strangely enough, they were in a comic book:

"Phoebe looks down on all these pink houses nestled in the gentle hills and valleys of Los Angeles. She reflects upon life: What does it all mean?"

No doubt someone looking at our world from the outside and seeing what we have done to it would ask themselves the same question about humanity and life: " What does it all mean?"

对我来说，设计还包含道德层面的职责。也就是说，好的设计是一种价值观。

The remit of design has an ethical dimension for me. Good design is a value.

我们必须牢记要建设更美好的世界这个道德价值观。

The better world that we have to build must be made with moral values in mind.

这个理念与人们对设计的普遍认识——轻松的娱乐活动大不相同。当前的主流观点认为，从产品到音乐、建筑、广告、电视节目，任何东西都必须能够立即吸引目标受众。

This approach is very different from the all too widespread attitude that treats design as some kind of light entertainment. According to prevailing opinion, everything, from products to music, architecture, advertising, TV shows or whatever, has to be made to have instant appeal to its target audience.

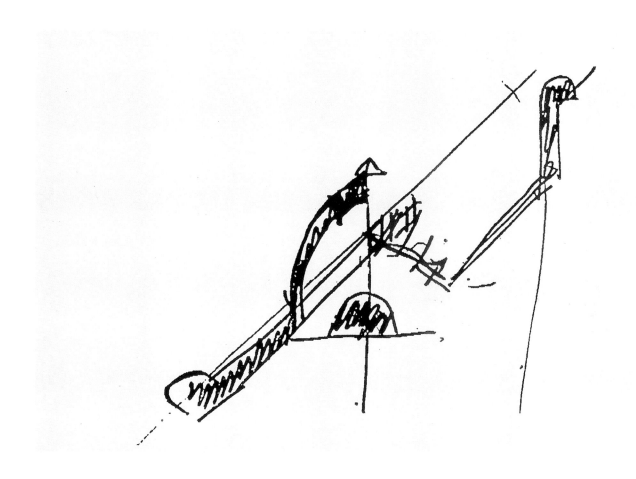

这样的抽象草图（便携式音响系统的一部分，参见第99页和第100页）显然是对未来思考方式的尝试。它可以被看作是一个标志，标志着设计所面临的挑战及寻找有意义的未来解决方案的难度。

Apparently abstract sketches like this one (which is part of a study for a portable music system, p. 99 and 100) illustrate attempts to think a way into the future. It can be seen as a symbol for the challenging tests that lie ahead for design and for how difficult it is to find future solutions.

这意味着只要能吸引人的就是好的，为了达成目的可以不择手段。这是后现代时期对任何价值观与社会责任近乎愤世嫉俗的漠视。

Good is what appeals. The triumph of 'anything goes'. That is the almost cynical indifference of the postmodern era towards any obligation to values.

主流观点这面大旗所掩盖的事情还不只这些，它还试图不惜一切代价让自己显得与众不同，并讽刺地嘲弄了从功能主义发展而来的现代美学。根据我的经验，刻意为了追求不同而不同的东西很少会是更好的，但更好的东西几乎总是不同的。

This umbrella covers much that, trying to be different at any price, ironically mocks the modern aesthetic that developed from the functional. In my experience, things that are different for difference's sake are seldom better, but things that are better are almost always different.

许多人仍然相信自己能忍受各种各样的愚蠢行为，包括草率的设计。他们认为这涉及的风险很小，未来的技术将会弥补已形成的损害。

这种致命的误解常来自那些普遍被认为受过教育的人。为什么他们的教育是如此有限呢？是傲慢吗？据我所知，真正受过教育的人从不傲慢而是谦虚，同时又具有批判性、专注性和敏锐的洞察力。他们能够认识到什么是错误的，能够看清楚那些无论怎样都会发生但其实不应该被允许发生的事情。同时，他们也可以预见由此必然会引发的后果。

我想以谦虚、批判、敏锐的理性思维去决定自己的命运。如果我们在做决定时能够完全出自理性，或是主要依据理性来做出判断，那么我们其实远不必与那么多先前固有的观点、成见、无关的考虑或非理性的恐惧做斗争。这样我们将向前迈出一大步。

改变社会面貌是较困难的一件事，但如果我们能够改进思维，那将是一个巨大的成就。而设计首先就是一个思维过程。

"新现代"意味着网络化思维、全球意识及将技术简化至人们可以控制的程度。在我们的社会中，新维度的设计发展将会为我们提供衡量生活品质的参考基准。

想让设计能够在所有的生活领域中得到一致性落实的前提条件是人们对公共生活的所有领域都具有适当的敏感性。只有当我们在社会的各个层面上理解和接受设计，我们才能通过设计实现生活质量的可持续提高。

因此，设计促进机构——德国设计委员会（German Design Council）必须代表全体人民的利益。同时，它在推动城市环境设计方面也必须体现全体人民的政治利益。

Many people still believe that we can afford all sorts of foolishness – including thoughtless design. They think that the risks involved are small and that tomorrow's technologies will straighten out the damage.

A fatal misapprehension found commonly amongst those that are generally considered to be educated. Why is their education so limited? Is it arrogance? Someone who is truly educated is, in my understanding, never arrogant, but modest and at the same time critical, attentive and perceptive. They recognise what is wrong, that which happens anyway but shouldn't be allowed to, and they see what has to happen.

I want to throw in my lot with modest, critical, perceptive reason. If, when we make decisions that are exclusively or primarily concerned with the use of reason in a specific circumstance, we didn't have to struggle with so many prefabricated opinions, preconceptions, irrelevant considerations or irrational fears, that would be a big step forward.

It is difficult to improve morals. But it would be a tremendous achievement if we could improve thinking. Design is first and foremost a thinking process.

The "new modern" means networked thinking, global awareness and the reduction of technology to what we can control. The development of a new dimension for design in our society will provide the benchmark with which we evaluate our quality of life.

The consistent application of design to all areas of life presupposes an appropriate sensitisation in all areas of public life. Only when we create an understanding and acceptance of design in all levels of society will a sustainable improvement in living and the quality of life through design be possible.

The work of the institution for design promotion called the German Design Council must stand up for this in the interest of the entire population. At the same time it has to reflect a political interest in maintaining the quality of engagement with our designed environment.

这需要制造商、政府、所有部门和所有政治力量的共同支持，以便能够满足国内外行业、媒体和民众的需求。当然，这也是他们的责任和义务，包括通过设计发展经济的职责，以及对国外的设计推广和对德国国内设计发展的支持。

在这个高科技时代，设计将面临诸多全新的挑战。经济和生态之间的共生关系越来越密切，我们需要耗材少、耗时短的生产方法。

This will require the support of the manufacturers, the government, all the ministries and all political powers to efficiently meet the needs of industry, media and the population at home and abroad. This pertains to their responsibilities and duties towards business development through design and design promotion abroad as well as support for design development at home.

In this age of high technology, design will be confronted with many completely new challenges. There is a growing symbiosis between economics and ecology and we need to reduce both material and time-intensive production methods.

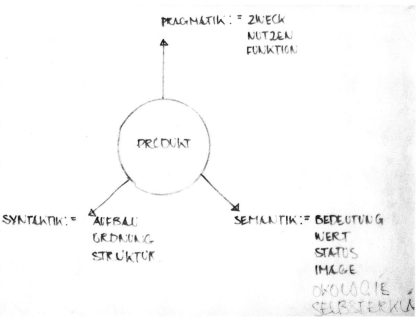

我们将如何从这场新形式的竞争中脱颖而出，取决于国家和欧洲经济领域未来生产效率的提高，取决于对于创新和技术发展的投资，取决于可行性生态概念的发展。在这个过程中，设计可以做出重大的贡献，并在所有这些领域发挥决定性作用，先决条件是为欧洲的设计发展制订有效的联合政治计划。值得一提的是，在未来的发展计划中还应将前东欧国家也纳入进来。

How we emerge from this new form of competition will be determined in the future by an increase in productive efficiency in the areas of national and European economics, investment in innovation and technological development as well as the development of viable ecological concepts. Design can make a significant contribution and take on a decisive role in all these areas. A prerequisite for this is the creation of an effective and joint political plan for design development in Europe that should include, in particular, the former eastern European nations in future concepts.

照片来源
Photo Credits

博朗公司和维瑟公司
Braun AG & Vitsoe

马克斯·博朗基金会
Max Braun Stiftung

蒂姆·劳特（Timm Rautert）
（第57—71页）
Timm Rautert (57–71)

格德 A. 穆勒（第18页）
Gerd A. Müller (22)

乔·克拉特
Jo Klatt

托马斯·迈耶档案馆（封面图片）
Thomas Mayer Archive
(Coverbild)

本书中相关产品的设计师名单

很少有产品是出自一位设计师之手，因为通常会有2位或2位以上设计师在不同阶段参与产品开发。

Designers of products featured in this book

It is not always possible to single out an individual designer as author of a specific product, since frequenthy two or more designers would work on its development at various stages.

页码	产品/课题	设计师
6	SK 4	汉斯·古格洛特, 迪特·拉姆斯
19	SK 4	汉斯·古格洛特, 迪特·拉姆斯
19	transistor 1, PC 3	迪特·拉姆斯
19	atelier 1, L 1, studio 2	迪特·拉姆斯
19	LE 1, L 2, TP 1, T 4	迪特·拉姆斯
19	T 41, T 52	迪特·拉姆斯
20	KM 3, MX 3, MP 3	格德 A. 穆勒
20	Combi	迪特·拉姆斯, 格德 A. 穆勒
20	SM 3	格德 A. 穆勒
20	PA 1, EF 2, F 60, H 1	迪特·拉姆斯
24	SK 4	汉斯·古格洛特, 迪特·拉姆斯
25	RT 20	迪特·拉姆斯
26	atelier 1, L 1	迪特·拉姆斯
27	KM 3, MX 3, MP 3, M 1	格德 A. 穆勒
27	PA 1	迪特·拉姆斯
28	T 41, P 1	迪特·拉姆斯
29	T3/T 31, T 4, T 41	迪特·拉姆斯
30	H 1, T 521, T 2	迪特·拉姆斯
31	studio 2, LE 1	迪特·拉姆斯
32	CS 11, CV 11, CE 11	迪特·拉姆斯
33	LE 1	迪特·拉姆斯
34	audio 1	迪特·拉姆斯
35	电视机的设计研究	迪特·拉姆斯
36	TS 45, TG 60, L 450	迪特·拉姆斯
37	audio 2, TG 60, FS 600	迪特·拉姆斯
38	studio 1000, TG 1000	迪特·拉姆斯
39	Ela 高保真系统	迪特·拉姆斯
39	示波器的设计研究	迪特·拉姆斯
40	电路产品"通向按钮的路"的设计研究	迪特·拉姆斯, 于尔根·格雷贝尔
41	Lectron 教育玩具	迪特·拉姆斯, 于尔根·格雷贝尔
42	TV 1000	迪特·拉姆斯
42	T 1000	迪特·拉姆斯
43	Studiomaster 2150	彼得·施耐德, 彼得·哈特温

Page	Product/Subject	Designer
6	SK 4	Hans Gugelot, Dieter Rams
19	SK 4	Hans Gugelot, Dieter Rams
19	transistor 1, PC 3	Dieter Rams
19	atelier 1, L 1, studio 2	Dieter Rams
19	LE 1, L 2, TP 1, T 4	Dieter Rams
19	T 41, T 52	Dieter Rams
20	KM 3, MX 3, MP 3	Gerd A. Müller
20	Combi	Dieter Rams, Gerd A. Müller
20	SM 3	Gerd A. Müller
20	PA 1, EF 2, F 60, H 1	Dieter Rams
24	SK 4	Hans Gugelot, Dieter Rams
25	RT 20	Dieter Rams
26	atelier 1, L 1	Dieter Rams
27	KM 3, MX 3, MP 3, M 1	Gerd A. Müller
27	PA 1	Dieter Rams
28	T 41, P 1	Dieter Rams
29	T3/T 31, T 4, T 41	Dieter Rams
30	H 1, T 521, T 22	Dieter Rams
31	studio 2, LE 1	Dieter Rams
32	CS 11, CV 11, CE 11	Dieter Rams
33	LE 1	Dieter Rams
34	audio 1	Dieter Rams
35	Designstudie TV	Dieter Rams
36	TS 45, TG 60, L 450	Dieter Rams
37	audio 2, TG 60, FS 600	Dieter Rams
38	studio 1000, TG 1000	Dieter Rams
39	Hi–Fi Ela system	Dieter Rams
39	Designstudie Oszillog.	Dieter Rams
40	Designstudie 'Der Weg zum Kopf'	Dieter Rams, Jürgen Greubel
41	Lectron	Dieter Rams, Jürgen Greubel
42	TV 1000	Dieter Rams
42	T 1000	Dieter Rams
43	Studiomaster 2150	Peter Schneider, Peter Hartwein